*Cooperative Learning*

# Wee Science

Laura Candler
In consultation with Laurie Kagan

# Kagan

**Kagan Publishing**
981 Calle Amanecer
San Clemente, CA 92673-6238
**1(800) 933-2667**
**www.KaganOnline.com**

ISBN: 978-1-879097-25-4

# Table of Contents

## Chapters

Table of Structures......................ii
Table of Process Skills ..............iii
Table of Blackline Masters ........iv
Table of Icons .............................v
Foreword....................................vii
Acknowledgements ....................ix

1. Introduction — 1
2. Cooperative Learning in the Early Grades — 5
3. Wee Science Structures — 15
4. Cooperative Process Science — 49

## Lessons

1. Catch A Rainbow — 63
2. Magnet Magic — 75
3. What's the Sense? — 91
4. Learning with Leaves — 99
5. Exploring Electricity — 111
6. Wonders of the Rain Forest — 127
7. Seeds of all Sorts — 147
8. Mystery Sounds — 163
9. Something's Fishy — 173
10. Helicopter Capers — 187
11. Rounding Up Rocks — 203
12. Temperature Predictions — 217

## Appendixes

Science Resources — 227
Bibliography of Children's Literature — 229

# Table of Structures

| Lesson | 1 | 2 | 3 | 4 | 5 | 6 | 7 | 8 | 9 | 10 | 11 | 12 |
|---|---|---|---|---|---|---|---|---|---|---|---|---|
| Blackboard Share (pg. 16) | ✔ | | | ✔ | | | | | | | | |
| Cooperative Play (pg. 18) | ✔ | ✔ | | ✔ | | ✔ | ✔ | ✔ | | ✔ | ✔ | |
| Corners (pg. 20) | | | | | | | | | | ✔ | | |
| Formations (pg. 22) | | | | | ✔ | | | | | | | |
| Line-Ups (pg. 24) | ✔ | | | | | | | | | | ✔ | |
| Mix-Freeze-Pair (pg. 26) | ✔ | ✔ | ✔ | | | ✔ | | | | | | |
| Numbered Heads Together (pg. 28) | | | | ✔ | | | | | ✔ | | | |
| Pairs (pg. 30) | | | ✔ | ✔ | ✔ | ✔ | ✔ | ✔ | | ✔ | ✔ | ✔ |
| RoundRobin (pg. 32) | | ✔ | ✔ | | | | ✔ | ✔ | | ✔ | ✔ | ✔ |
| RoundTable (pg. 34) | | ✔ | ✔ | | ✔ | ✔ | ✔ | | ✔ | | ✔ | |
| Send-A-Problem (pg. 36) | | ✔ | ✔ | | | | | | | | | |
| Team Discussion (pg. 38) | | | | ✔ | | | | | ✔ | | | |
| Team Interview (pg. 40) | | | | | | | | ✔ | | | | |
| Team Projects (pg. 42) | ✔ | | | ✔ | | ✔ | | ✔ | ✔ | | ✔ | ✔ |
| Think-Pair-Share (pg. 46) | | ✔ | ✔ | ✔ | ✔ | ✔ | ✔ | ✔ | | ✔ | | ✔ |

Laura Candler: *Wee Science*      *Kagan Publishing* • 1 (800) 933-2667 • www.KaganOnline.com

# Table of Process Skills

| Lesson | 1 | 2 | 3 | 4 | 5 | 6 | 7 | 8 | 9 | 10 | 11 | 12 |
|---|---|---|---|---|---|---|---|---|---|---|---|---|
| Classifying | | | | | | ✔ | ✔ | | | | ✔ | |
| Communicating | ✔ | ✔ | ✔ | ✔ | ✔ | ✔ | ✔ | ✔ | ✔ | ✔ | ✔ | ✔ |
| Experimenting | | ✔ | | | | | ✔ | | | ✔ | | ✔ |
| Identifying | ✔ | | ✔ | ✔ | | ✔ | ✔ | ✔ | ✔ | | ✔ | |
| Inferring | ✔ | ✔ | ✔ | | ✔ | | ✔ | ✔ | ✔ | ✔ | | ✔ |
| Measuring | | | | ✔ | | | | | | | ✔ | ✔ |
| Model Making | ✔ | | | | ✔ | | | | ✔ | ✔ | | ✔ |
| Observing | ✔ | ✔ | ✔ | ✔ | ✔ | ✔ | ✔ | ✔ | ✔ | ✔ | ✔ | ✔ |
| Organizing Data | ✔ | ✔ | | ✔ | | ✔ | ✔ | | | ✔ | ✔ | |
| Predicting | | ✔ | ✔ | ✔ | | ✔ | | | | ✔ | ✔ | ✔ |

# Table of Blackline Masters

| Title of Blackline Master | Lesson | Title of Blackline Master | Lesson |
|---|---|---|---|
| Advanced Animal Sorting | 6 | Make A Fish | 9 |
| Advanced Seed Sorting | 7 | Object Signs | 2 |
| Amazing Maze | 2 | On My Listening Walk I Heard | 8 |
| Basic Helicopters | 10 | Our Leaf Lengths | 4 |
| Color A Rainbow | 1 | Our Rock Hunting Rules | 11 |
| Dear Parents | 6 | Parts Of A Fish | 9 |
| Demonstration Rainbow | 1 | Parts Of A Seed | 7 |
| Directions for Magnetic Toys | 2 | Rain Forest Animal Cards | 6 |
| Electrical Items | 5 | Rain Forest Of The Earth | 6 |
| Experiment Helicopters | 10 | Rocky Weights | 11 |
| Fish Diagram | 9 | Simple Animal Sorting | 6 |
| Fish Part Word Cards | 9 | Simple Seed Sorting | 7 |
| Fishy Observations | 9 | Simple Ways To Light A Bulb | 5 |
| From The Heart Of The Rain Forest | 6 | Thermometer Predictions | 12 |
| Helicopter Experiment | 10 | Things That Fly | 10 |
| Leaf Patterns | 4 | Types Of Bean Seeds | 7 |
| Magnet Signs | 2 | What's In The Bag? | 3 |
| Magnetic Attractions | 2 | Which Bulbs Will Light? | 5 |

# Table of Icons

 **Adaptations for Age**

This symbol denotes lesson modifications for very young children as well as adaptations for older students.

 **Advanced Preparation**

This symbol is located throughout all lessons to indicate advanced preparation is needed for specific activities.

 **Content Ideas**

The lightbulb icon denotes quick and easy ideas for using cooperative learning structures with science content.

 **Curriculum Links**

Look for the links icon when you need ideas for extending science concepts into other curriculum areas.

 **Learning Center**

This symbol denotes activities that can be easily modified for use in a learning center.

 **Literature Link**

Look for the open book icon next to activities which use children's literature.

 **Safety Spotlight**

Be sure to read the safety reminders next to the spotlight icon in many lessons.

 **Science Journal Ideas**

You'll find the journal icon at the end of each lesson adjacent to specific journal writing ideas.

 **Structure Variations**

You'll find useful information about cooperative learning structure variations next to this symbol.

# Foreword

We at **Kagan Publishing** are quite proud to publish *Wee Science*. Consistent with the Cooperative Learning philosophy, the book represents the creativity and hard work of a team: Laura Candler, author; Laurie Kagan, project consultant; Celso Rodriguez, designer and artist; and Michael Cifranic, formatter.

Laura and Laurie worked together integrating the best of cooperative learning with the best of process science. Without the brilliant and hard work of Celso and Mike, the wonderful ideas of Laura and Laurie could not appear in such an attractive, teacher-friendly format.

Successful science instruction involves learning both **scientific knowledge** and **scientific process** — attitudes, ways of thinking, methods. At the heart of *Wee Science* is a belief in the foundational importance of scientific process. The success of science education rests on our ability and willingness to "do science" with our students.

Our success as science educators from kindergarten on is a function of how well we teach the process of science — the attitudes, skills, ways of thinking, and methods of science. If we teach process well, scientific knowledge will follow.

It is because of this belief in process that Laura begins by identifying ten key process skills of primary science: *Classifying, Communicating, Experimenting, Identifying, Inferring, Measuring, Model Making, Observing, Organizing Data*, and *Predicting*. In each of her model lessons she explicitly includes at least four of the ten process skills. The content of science is taught, but only in the context of meaningful, hands-on experimentation.

With her "curriculum links" Laura provides broader context as well, relating each science lesson to diverse areas such as art, health, language arts, creative movement, literature, music, social studies, math, as well as journal writing. In this way science is taught in a context which gives it meaning. Laura's extensively field-tested lessons leave primary students demanding to "do more science."

If we go the other route, if we emphasize scientific knowledge over scientific process, students learn neither. We will continue to produce generations of students "turned off" toward science. Our traditional approach to science has reduced science to dull, non-relevant history. It is not a surprise that we have a nation which is not scientifically literate. "One only has to look at the international studies of educational performance to see that U.S. students rank near the bottom in science and mathematics — hardly what one would expect if the schools were doing their job well." (American Association for the Advancement of Science, 1989, p. 13).

*Wee Science* is an antidote to traditional science textbooks which emphasize content over process:
> "The present science textbooks and methods of instruction, far from helping, often actually impede progress toward scientific literacy. They emphasize the learning of answers more than the exploration of questions, memory at the expense of of critical thought, bits and pieces of information instead of understandings in context, recitation over argument, reading in lieu of doing. They fail to encourage students to work together, to share ideas and information freely with each other, or to use modern instruments to extend their intellectual capabilities." (American Association for the Advancement of Science, 1989, p. 14).

*Wee Science* turns the table on the traditional approach to science education: At the top of the agenda are exploration of questions, critical thought, collaborative effort, contextual understanding, discussion, and hands-on manipulation. *Wee Science* nourishes students' inherent love of science, nourishment which, if made more common, will prepare our society with the scientific literacy necessary for healthy functioning in our increasingly technological world.

Dr. Spencer Kagan

**Reference**
American Association for the Advancement of Science. *Science for All Americans. A Project 2061 Report on Literacy Goals in Science, Mathematics, and Technology.* American Association for the Advancement of Science. Washington, D.C., 1989.

# Acknowledgements

Many people have contributed to *Wee Science*. Some have shared cooperative learning techniques and ideas for lessons. Others have critiqued the lessons or tested those ideas in classrooms. Their enthusiastic support encouraged me throughout this project.

First of all, I would like to thank **Dr. Spencer Kagan** for his dedicated work in the field of cooperative learning. He never stops striving to perfect cooperative learning and he is always open to new ideas. His structural approach to cooperative learning provides the foundation for this book. I am grateful for his guidance and support.

I also want to thank **Laurie Kagan** for reading my lessons and giving me valuable feedback. Her insightful comments have left a definite mark on this book.

Two other members of the Kagan team have been instrumental to the success of this book. I am extremely grateful to designer and artist **Celso Rodriguez.** Along with creating the cover, Celso has done an impressive job of designing the layout and illustrations for Wee Science. Each character he created conveys the joy of science discovery, infusing the text with warmth and energy. I also appreciate the dedication and hard-work of **Michael Cifranic** who spent innumerable hours formatting Wee Science on his computer. He has been extremely patient with me through untold revisions and corrections. Together, these two brought my words to life and shaped this book into a dynamic and user-friendly teaching tool. Thanks Mike and Celso!

I want to express my appreciation to **Karen Zimmerman** for her expertise in early childhood education. She introduced me to developmentally appropriate practices and helped me adapt my cooperative learning lessons to the primary classroom. Furthermore, she tested lessons with her kindergarten students. I could not have written this book without her constant guidance.

I also want to thank the many other teachers who tried my lessons in their own classrooms. Because of them, I can truly say that the Wee Science lessons are child-tested. I appreciate all the suggestions these teachers shared with me after trying lessons with their children. Many thanks to **Donna Albaugh, Brenda Angell, Dorine Beauchamp, Brenda Bethea, Barbara Burgess, Cheryl Collazo, Cathie Cuffman, Kathy Howell, Mel Jenkins, Michelle Laferte, Monika Morse, Sue Moyer, Pat King, Tobie Meyer, Deborah O'Neil, Rachel Pinkham, Jenny Scott, Becky Steadman, Maggie Spivey, Gladys White, Joan Zeberlein,** and **Kami Zimmerman.** I also wish to thank **Deborah Dees, Jean Williams,** and **Kay Mitchell** for inviting me into their classrooms to test lessons. I am grateful to **Kathy Kennedy,** Principal of Glendale Elementary and former Assistant Principal of J.W. Seabrook Elementary, for sharing the lessons with her teachers and giving me feedback on their progress. In addition, I appreciate the continued support of **Donald Dawson,** Principal of E.E. Miller Elementary, who has challenged me as a teacher and believed in me as a writer.

I want to thank my friend **Aleka Munroe** for her support and encouragement throughout this writing project. She read my manuscript with a critical eye and offered many valuable suggestions for its improvement.

Last, but certainly not least, I want to thank my husband **Marco Candler** for helping me find time to write. Without his support, *Wee Science* would still be a dream rather than a reality.

*Laura Candler*

Laura Candler

# Chapter 1

## Introduction

Children are natural scientists. Like scientists, children constantly seek answers and make discoveries. Their curiosity is a tangible force that won't be denied. Scientists and children alike are relentless in their quest for understanding; yet, both discover that answers only lead to more questions.

Our role as teachers is to foster that restless spirit of curiosity. We must view the world through a child's eyes and become learners as well as teachers. We must share their delight in learning and encourage their explorations. Furthermore, we must provide them with opportunities to discover the science all around them.

Science educators are proclaiming something that primary teachers have long known: children learn by doing. In science instruction, increasing emphasis is being placed on teaching process skills. Very simply, process science means doing science. The American Association for the

Advancement of Science is currently spearheading a curriculum reform entitled "Project 2061." This long-term project outlines what students need to know to become scientifically literate and suggests ways to reach those goals. Their first report, *Science For All Americans*, advocates the importance of hands-on instruction by stating,

*Students need to get acquainted with the things around them - including devices, organisms, materials, shapes, and numbers - and to observe them, collect them, handle them, describe them, become puzzled by them, ask questions about them, argue about them, and then to try*

to find answers to their questions.
(Rutherford & Ahlgren, 1990)

Recent science reforms also clearly state the need for cooperative learning in the science classroom. The most recent Project 2061 report, *Benchmarks for Science Literacy*, states,

*Science should begin in Kindergarten with students learning to work in small teams (rather than as isolated individuals) to ask and answer questions about their surroundings and to share findings with others.*
(AAAS, 1993)

Adding cooperative learning to process instruction results in "cooperative process science," or doing science together. For scientists, part of the joy of discovery comes from sharing findings with colleagues. Children experience the same need to share discoveries with their peers. The wonder of learning is multiplied when children do science together. Cooperative learning fosters a warm, caring atmosphere in which children can share ideas freely.

Early childhood educators know that children need a blend of freedom and structure in the classroom. Children need some freedom to explore their own ideas and make discoveries in their own ways. Yet children also need to be guided toward understanding

specific science concepts. Cooperative process science provides the tools to accomplish both.

To help you teach basic science concepts, I have developed a dozen multi-structural lessons based on themes commonly taught in the primary classroom. Each lesson introduces a concept and develops it through cooperative activities. Though many activities are highly structured, most lessons provide time for unstructured cooperative play with manipulatives. Some lessons require as little as a few days to complete, while others may last several weeks.

Because I realize that you have many wonderful ideas of your own, a second objective of this book is to guide you in developing your own science lessons. If you are not familiar with cooperative learning basics, I suggest you start by reading Chapter 2, "Cooperative Learning in the Early Grades." This chapter introduces basic concepts and shows you how to set up a cooperative classroom. Next, skim the structure descriptions to get a feel for the variety of techniques available. Read Chapter 4, "Cooperative Process Science", for an overview of the process skills and elements of science instruction.

Finally, choose a simple lesson such as "Helicopter Capers" and try it with your students. Study the way the lesson introduces a concept and develops it with cooperative techniques. All lessons are multi-structural, meaning that a variety of structures is used to teach each concept. Don't try to modify the lessons at first; every lesson was carefully designed to incorporate the basic elements of cooperative learning and science instruction.

After teaching several lessons exactly as they were written, try developing a lesson centered around your own science ideas and activities. Start with a simple "hook" activity to capture your students' interest. Use another cooperative technique to introduce the science concept you want to teach. Be sure to include activities to explore the concept further and check students' understanding. Don't expect to complete this type of science lesson in one class period. Students need time to play with manipulatives and discuss new concepts. For more information on the structural approach to writing lessons, read Spencer Kagan's *Cooperative Learning*. In particular, read the chapter entitled "Co-op Lesson Planning."

*Wee Science* blends cooperative learning, process skill experiences, and child-centered instruction. Whether you teach the lessons in this book or develop your own, I invite you to share in the excitement of wee science!

**References**
**American Association for the Advancement of Science.** *Benchmarks for Science Literacy.* Oxford University Press, New York, NY: 1993.

**Kagan, Spencer.** *Cooperative Learning. Kagan Publishing,* San Clemente CA: 1994.

**Rutherford, J. & Ahlgren, A.** *Science for All Americans.* Oxford University Press, New York, NY: 1990.

# Chapter 2

# Cooperative Learning in the Early Grades

**Cooperative Learning vs. Group Work** ◆

**Cooperative Learning Structures** ◆

**Team Formation** ◆

**Seating Arrangements** ◆

**Classroom Management** ◆

**Social Skills** ◆

**Developmentally Appropriate Practices** ◆

**Learning Centers** ◆

Cooperative learning methods are radically different from "traditional" teaching methods. If you aren't already using cooperative learning in your classroom, you'll need to become familiar with these new teaching techniques before attempting a full science lesson.

Since the focus of this book is on the science classroom, I'll only include an overview of the essential components of cooperative learning. If you haven't had any instruction in Kagan's structural approach, I suggest reading his book Cooperative Learning. Furthermore, I recommend that primary teachers read Cooperative Learning Lessons for Little Ones by Lorna Curran to learn how cooperative learning is implemented in the lower grades. I also recommend taking one of Dr. Kagan's teacher training workshops so that you can experience the power of cooperative learning firsthand.

I have found that many teachers ask the same questions when setting up a cooperative classroom. In this chapter I will answer those questions, focusing specifically on the cooperative science classroom. Basically, teachers want to know:

- *How is cooperative learning different from "group work"?*
- *What is a cooperative learning structure?*
- *How do I form teams in my classroom?*
- *How should I seat my students?*
- *How do I manage cooperative learning activities?*
- *How can I teach my children to work together?*
- *Is cooperative learning developmentally appropriate for young children?*
- *Can cooperative learning be integrated into a "learning center" approach?*

## Cooperative Learning vs. Group Work

Believe it or not, cooperative learning is not a new concept. For decades teachers have experimented with allowing students to work in teams. However, many teachers discovered that cooperative learning was wonderful in theory but disastrous in practice. The bright students were doing all the work, students were unable to cooperate with each other, and teachers had no way to evaluate who was actually learning. Many of us remember at least one incident in school where we worked in groups. In most cases our experiences only reinforce our ideas that cooperative learning is just an old idea that sounds great but doesn't work.

If you have ever felt this way, don't despair. These situations involve group work, but have little to do with cooperative learning! True cooperative learning involves students actively working together in a caring, concerned environment. In addition, true cooperative activities are structured so that all students participate equally and are held accountable for their learning.

Cooperative learning theory and practice have undergone radical changes in the last 15 years. Educators and theorists have identified the essential components of cooperative learning which distinguish it from simple "group work." Understanding these basic concepts will help you implement true cooperative learning in your own classroom.

## Four Basic Principles of Cooperative Learning

Kagan has identified four basic principles which are fundamental to the success of any cooperative learning activity: Simultaneous Interaction, Positive Interdependence, Individual Accountability, and Equal Participation. These basic principles provide the foundation for successful cooperative learning activities. A brief overview of each basic principle is given, but true understanding and appreciation for these principles will come only through using them and observing their impact in your classroom.

### 1. Simultaneous Interaction

Simultaneous Interaction is the principle that separates cooperative learning from traditional teaching methods. In the traditional setting, participation is usually sequential, with one person at a time actively involved in learning. For instance, in a class discussion one student at a time shares an idea with the class. The rest of the class may or may not be involved; the activity is considered successful as long as one person at a time is talking.

Contrast this with a **Team Discussion** in which one person on each team is talking simultaneously. With teams of four, 25% of the class is speaking and 75% of the class is actively listening. A **Pair Discussion** allows for even greater simultaneous interaction. When two students are discussing an idea together, one person in each pair is actively involved. The amount of student involvement in the class jumps to 50% at this point!

Keep in mind, however, that greater simultaneity may not always meet the lesson objectives. You'll still use class discussions when the ideas being discussed need to be heard by all students or to correct misunderstandings about science concepts.

Simultaneous Interaction is a powerful principle to apply in planning your instruction. In general, simultaneous interaction is preferable to sequential interaction because it increases the number of students actively involved.

### 2. Positive Interdependence

A spirit of positive interdependence is evident when students feel that they need each other in order to accomplish the assigned task. They feel that a gain for one is a gain for all and that the task can only be completed if everyone participates.

One way to foster Positive Interdependence is to limit and assign the resources available so that everyone must contribute to the final product. One person may have the scissors, another the glue, another the marker, etc. With team projects such as murals and posters, you can assign each team member one color and tell students that ALL colors must be used in the final product. You can also divide the task so that each person has a specific part to complete. The assignment can't be finished without everyone doing his or her share.

### 3. Individual Accountability

Early attempts at cooperative learning often failed because students were not held accountable for participating and/or learning. When looking at a group product such as a poster, a teacher had no idea who participated. Other cooperative learning activities with no tangible products gave even fewer clues about who was learning and who was not.

Just being aware of the importance of Individual Accountability will help prevent these pitfalls in your own classroom. First of all, activities should be structured in such a way that everyone must contribute to the discussion or task. As mentioned above, color coding products or dividing responsibilities is helpful.

Secondly, students must still be evaluated individually in order to find out if they have learned a concept. Since formal testing is limited in most primary classrooms, informal assessments should be used frequently. Simply taking time to observe and talk to individual children will help you determine what they have learned. Having them keep Science Journals will also encourage Individual Accountability.

## 4. Equal Participation

In the best cooperative learning activities, everyone participates equally in each discussion or task. Not only does each child have some part in the final product, each child makes an equal contribution to that product. In a discussion, each team member talks for the same amount of time. In a science experiment, children share the work equally.

Equal Participation is an important concept in the early grades. It's not that some children don't want

to participate; the problem is that everyone wants to do everything! Learning to share and take turns must be taught, and cooperative learning activities provide the perfect opportunity to practice those skills.

## Cooperative Learning Structures

At this point you may be wondering how you'll ever implement cooperative learning in your own classroom successfully. How will you ensure that the four basic principles are integrated throughout your science lessons?

The answer lies in Dr. Spencer Kagan's Structural Approach in which lessons are built with cooperative learning "structures." Structures are not tied to subject matter but rather provide ways to implement cooperative learning techniques. Examples of basic structures include **Think-Pair-Share, RoundRobin,** and **Numbered Heads Together.** Cooperative learning structures are designed to incorporate the four basic principles, allowing you the freedom to plan your lessons without worrying about including these principles. As long as you build your lessons with structures, you'll automatically incorporate those four essential components of cooperative learning.

Each science lesson in this book is "multi-structural," comprising a variety of cooperative learning structures. As you teach the lessons you'll see the same structures used over and over in many different ways. To assist you in using the structures correctly, an entire chapter has been devoted to understanding and using cooperative learning structures. For each structure used in this book, you'll find an explanation of the specific steps you should follow when using that structure. You'll also find tips for adapting the structure to different age levels and suggestions for incorporating other science content.

## Team Formation

Before you begin teaching science cooperatively, you'll need to form heterogeneous teams. Teams of four students are preferable since they can easily be divided for pair work. Unless otherwise stated, the science lessons in this book assume you've divided your class into teams of four and have assigned partners within those teams for pair work.

Careful consideration should be given to forming cooperative learning teams. Teams should be balanced with regards to academic ability, ethnic background, and gender. In general, students should not be allowed to choose their own teams.

Every teacher has his or her favorite method of forming teams. I'll share one method with you, but if you feel the need for more information on this subject you may want to read the chapter in *Kagan Cooperative Learning* on team formation.

Since you'll be forming teams of boys and girls with varying abilities and ethnic backgrounds, you'll need an organized system for planning those teams. Using manipulatives such as index cards is helpful. You'll find one easy way of forming teams (right).

Steps in Forming Teams of Four
1. Gather the following supplies:
A copy of your class roster
Four crayons or markers
(blue, green, yellow and red)
A pencil or pen
A stack of index cards
(one per student)

2. Write one student's name on the top line of each index card. If necessary, use the rest of the card for notes about the student.

| Latoya Johnson |
| --- |
| |
| - strong leader |
| - needs help with math |
| |
| |

3. Divide the index cards into four equal piles based on student ability and/or developmental level. Place the high ability students in one pile, the high-average students in another, the low-average students in a third, and the low ability students in the fourth pile. Make sure the piles are approximately equal in size. If you have 28 students, you'll have 7 cards in each pile. If you have 30 students you'll have 7 cards in some piles and 8 cards in the other stacks.

4. Color-code the four piles by drawing a large dot of the appropriate color in the upper right-hand corner of each index card. Use the colors given below:

Blue:   High-ability students
Green: High-average students
Yellow: Low-average students
Red: Low-ability students

5. Clear a large work area on the table or floor. Start by placing all the blue cards in a column. Think of these students as the academic leaders of your teams.

6. Place the green, yellow, and red cards in columns next to the blue cards.

7. If your cards do not evenly divide into four columns, decide whether you want some teams to have three or five students. Classroom size and the nature of the lesson will play a part in this decision.

8. Each row of cards represents one team. Examine each row carefully to see if your teams are balanced according to race and gender. If some are not, switch cards so that your final teams are as balanced as possible.

9. Number your teams and write the team numbers on each card.

10. Draw a seating chart or make a list of team assignments to share with your students. Do not let students see the index cards you used in planning teams.

If you don't want to bother with index cards, a Team Formation Kit is available from **Kagan Publishing.** The kit contains color-coded cards, plain cards, slotted sheets of tagboard for displaying the teams, and full directions.

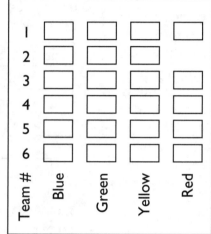

Many teachers also want to know how long their teams should stay together. Students in the upper grades generally stay together six weeks. However, most primary teachers find this amount of time too long for young children. Their one-on-one relationships at this age are constantly changing. Friendships form and dissolve on a daily basis. Young children find it difficult to commit to a long-term relationship with three other children. The concept of "team" has to be developed over time.

At first, you may want to form new teams each time you start a new science activity. Many of the lessons take several days and provide a natural point for dissolving a team and creating a new one. As the year progresses, you can leave children in teams for longer periods of time. By the end of second grade, students should be able to handle staying in teams for a month or more.

Sometimes you may want to form random teams for a single activity or for a day. To form random teams, shuffle your index cards together without regard for the color-coding and deal the cards into stacks of four students. Announce the students on each random team. When the activity is over, allow students to reunite with their "old" teammates. Using random teams in this way adds a spark of excitement and can build class unity.

## Seating Arrangements

The next consideration after forming teams is how to best seat students. If your classroom is equipped with tables, seat each team of four at one table so that no one has his or her back to the front of the room. If you have flat-topped desks, four desks may be pushed together to form a table. This arrangement is ideal for the science classroom since it provides a flat surface for convenience during science activities. The desks may be separated during testing or other individual activities.

Probably the most difficult furniture to work with is the L-shaped slant-top desk. The desks don't fit together easily to form a table, and even when pushed together the resulting surface is not flat. Activities with batteries, marbles, and containers of water become difficult to perform. Yet inadequate furniture should never be an excuse for not doing cooperative learning! The creative teacher can always find a solution. One easy way to solve the problem is to have students sit on the floor when a flat surface is required. Another is to move the activity outside or to a different room, such as the cafeteria.

## Classroom Management

One reason many teachers hesitate to implement cooperative learning is a concern that the resulting noise and activity will be difficult to manage. It's a lot easier to manage a classroom when only one student at a time is allowed to speak. As teachers we like to feel "in control" of our class, and we feel that allowing many students to interact at once will become a management nightmare.

These concerns, in fact, are very valid. If a teacher tries to implement cooperative learning without adequate management strategies, the classroom environment can dissolve into a free-for-all of unstructured noise and activity.

Fortunately, there are a host of simple classroom management ideas which allow teachers to control the activity level without stifling the excitement of learning. Some techniques can be used in any situation, while others are more appropriate for particular activities.

Implementing a Quiet Signal is the first step towards managing the activity level in your classroom. Nothing ruins the spirit of a cooperative activity more than having to constantly yell above your students' voices to get their attention. One effective signal is to simply raise your hand when you want students to be quiet. As students see you with your hand raised, they become quiet and raise their hands also. Before long, everyone will silently have a hand in the air. Wait until everyone is ready before speaking. I use this signal frequently, but I have modified it a bit. Sometimes students are so intent on their tasks that I may stand with my hand raised for 30 seconds before anyone realizes that I want their attention. I now count softly, "One . . . two . . three. . . . " My students know they are to be quiet and looking at me by the time I say "three."

Another management strategy is to plan your activities so thoroughly that students don't have the opportunity to develop off-task behaviors. Give clear, bite-sized directions. When possible, use one team to model or demonstrate the activity. Have all materials prepared and counted out for each team in advance.

Give positive attention to behaviors you want to develop. Rather than constantly reprimanding teams that are too loud or not working well together, compliment the teams that are behaving in a desired manner. Simply stand beside a team that is working well, use your quiet signal, and tell the class what you like about the behavior of that team. For example, "I like the way this team has their heads close together while they talk. They can hear each other but they aren't disturbing other teams." Try to find something positive to say about each team.

As you become comfortable with cooperative learning, you'll discover many more techniques to help you manage instruction effectively.

## Social Skills

Some teachers have told me that they would like to try cooperative learning, but they are afraid their students won't get along in teams. They feel that too much time will be wasted while team members argue with each other instead of working productively together.

Once again, these are very valid concerns. You can't just seat four young children together who have nothing in common and expect them to automatically treat each other with loving kindness. Many students lack the social skills necessary to work well with others. The skills to be successful in a group are very different from those needed to accomplish a task individually. These skills must be actively taught and reinforced.

For instance, students need to learn to respect each other's ideas. Cooperative learning requires a warm, caring, and supportive environment. I teach my students from the first day of school that "put downs" are not tolerated and that all ideas are valued. Students should never be allowed to express put downs in front of the class or within teams. In addition, students should be taught how to express praise for each others' accomplishments and ideas. In her book Cooperative Learning Lessons for Little Ones, Lorna Curran refers to this as "Happy Talk." All children can easily understand the concept of "Happy Talk;" however, many children need constant practice and reinforcement to master this social skill.

Students also need to learn the importance of active listening. These skills can easily be taught through role-playing. Ask a student volunteer to come forward to tell you some exciting news (arrange this in advance so they will know how you are going to react). Pretend to be completely uninterested by avoiding eye-contact, interrupting them, and fiddling with something like a pencil or watch. Then repeat the entire scenario using active listening skills (leaning toward the speaker, making eye-contact, asking relevant questions, etc.). Discuss the difference between poor listening and active listening.

In the same way, most social skills can be taught to students. Focus on one skill at a time, teaching students specific ways to improve that cooperative skill.

## Developmentally Appropriate Practices

Early childhood educators now advocate "developmentally appropriate practices" in the primary classroom. Teachers often ask if cooperative learning is appropriate for young children.

To answer this, let's examine the term "developmentally appropriate." A definitive source of information on this topic is Developmentally Appropriate Practice in Early Childhood Programs Serving Children From Birth Through Age 8, distributed by the National Association for the Education for Young Children. According to this source, "the concept of developmental appropriateness has two dimensions: age appropriateness and individual appropriateness." (NAEYC, 1987) To summarize, many educators believe that humans go through a fairly predictable sequence of physical, emotional, social, and cognitive developmental stages. Yet all children are unique individuals with different strengths, interests, and family backgrounds. When planning activities, teachers should consider both their students' developmental levels and their individual differences.

So, is cooperative learning developmentally appropriate for young children? The answer is that cooperative learning techniques are appropriate when used as a part of the child's total instruction. Even the strongest proponents of cooperative learning don't recommend that young children be kept in teams all day doing one structure after another. Children at this age need some time to initiate their own activities and pursue their own interests. They need a balance of large group, small group, and individual instruction.

However, acknowledging other types of instruction in no way diminishes the importance of cooperative learning. Even though children don't spend their entire day in small groups, the time they do work cooperatively is critical. Valuable social skills are developed through structured cooperative activities. One of the NAEYC recommendations is that children be given "many opportunities daily to develop social skills such as helping, cooperating, negotiating, and talking with the person involved to solve interpersonal problems." (NAEYC, 1987) Structured cooperative activities provide students with the opportunity to develop all of these skills.

## Learning Centers

Many teachers, especially those using developmentally appropriate practices, say that they can't use cooperative learning because their classroom is set up with learning centers. My response is that many cooperative learning activities can easily be modified for use in centers. In addition, learning centers have definite advantages in science. Most of the teachers who field-tested these lessons completed parts of each lesson in centers.

For instance, in the "Wonders of the Rain Forest" lesson you begin by reading The Great Kapok Tree to your class. You could easily tape the story and let students listen to it when they visit a center. The next part of the lesson requires children to cut apart and color Rain Forest Animal Cards, a task easily completed in centers. If your students have not done Venn diagrams, you'll probably still want to introduce this concept to the entire class at once. However, later your students could complete the guided practice with a partner in a learning center. Near the end of the lesson, your children sample foods from the rain forest. Why not place the foods in a center so that one team at a time can taste the foods and discuss them?

In science, learning centers are especially useful when materials are limited. If you only have one set of magnets, place them in a center. Introduce the activity to the entire class in the morning and let each team visit the center sometime during the day.

Learning centers can also be used when an activity requires close supervision. For example, the "Temperature Predictions" lesson involves constructing thermometers from soda bottles and straws. Young children may need help making their thermometers. If you place all the materials in a learning center, you can assist one team at a time. If you aren't able to stay with the center, try recruiting an assistant, volunteer, or older student to monitor it for you.

As you can see, cooperative learning techniques are definitely compatible with a learning center approach. To help you spot activities which are adaptable, I have placed a "Learning Center" icon next to the parts of each lesson that can be completed in a center.

Now, with your knowledge of cooperative learning basics, you are ready to set up a cooperative classroom. If you need more information on this topic, read Dr. Kagan's book *Kagan Cooperative Learning*, a comprehensive resource about the structural approach.

## References

**Curran, Lorna.** *Cooperative Learning Lessons for Little Ones.* ***Kagan Publishing,*** San Clemente, CA: 1993.

**Kagan, Spencer.** *Kagan Cooperative Learning.* ***Kagan Publishing,*** San Clemente, CA: 2009.

**National Association for the Education of Young Children.** *Developmentally Appropriate Practice in Early Childhood Programs Serving Children From Birth Through Age 8.* NAEYC, Washington, DC: 1987.

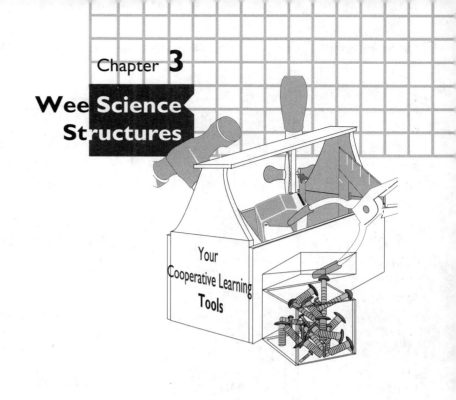

## Chapter 3

# Wee Science Structures

Structures are the tools which ensure your success with cooperative learning. The 15 structures which follow provide an array of cooperative learning techniques designed to meet the needs of every primary teacher. As when learning any new tool, practice is essential. Learn to use the structures correctly by experiencing them throughout the *Wee Science* lessons.

When you become familiar with the structures, you will want to use them to create your own science lessons. To assist you with lesson planning, content ideas are offered for each structure. Variations of each structure are provided to help you adapt them to your specific needs. After you discover the power of these tools, you'll find yourself reaching into your structure "toolbox" each time you prepare to build a new lesson!

① **Teacher Selects Sharing Method**

② **Team Members Share Ideas With Class**

**(See Lessons 1 and 4)**

**Blackboard Share** provides an excellent way for teams to share written information with the class. Students come to the blackboard to record results of an investigation or add data to a class graph.

Your
Cooperative Learning
*Tools*

## Teacher selects sharing method—

First, decide how you want your students to present their information. Try to choose a method which allows many students to record data at the same time. For instance, you can divide your chalkboard into sections and let each team write their results simultaneously. Or let each team rotate to the chalkboard during another activity so students aren't waiting for each other to share.

Create class bar graphs by sketching a blank graph on the board and having individuals or team representatives shade in results. Sometimes small sticky notes can be used to speed up the process of recording data.

**①**

## Team members share ideas with class—

When the time comes for students to share information, explain the procedure to the class. Allow students to come forward and contribute to the sharing activity. Follow with a class discussion to analyze the results of the activity.

**②**

### Sharing on Paper

Butcher paper, chart paper, or poster paper can substitute for board space. A long sheet of butcher paper can be used for class graphing activities. Poster paper works well when teams prepare their part of the class presentation separately. Students can complete the posters in teams, then tape their team posters to the wall for sharing.

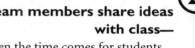

### Overhead Projector Share

If you teach with an overhead projector, you may want to draw the class chart on the overhead instead of on the board. You can also draw the chart in black ink on paper and burn a transparency. Students can write on the transparency with a non-permanent pen. After the activity, wipe the transparency clean and save it for another lesson.

• Reporting results from an experiment
• Sharing results of a team vote
• Creating a class bar graph
• Presenting team posters to the class
• Organizing data from a class survey

**①** **Teacher Provides Materials**

**②** **Students Play Together**

**(See Lessons 1, 2, 4, 5, 6, 7, 8, 10, and 11)**

**Cooperative Play** occurs when pairs or teams of children are given the freedom to explore science materials without direction. Play is an essential part of early grade instruction and has a definite place within the cooperative classroom. Through play, young children learn. Without structure or direction, they unknowingly use the very science process skills we strive to teach. Children at play observe, identify, classify, and communicate in order to discover the world around them.

**Cooperative Play** is an essential part of any hands-on science lesson. Young children have difficulty focusing on a science lesson when they are fascinated with the objects you have just placed in their hands. Allowing them to play with those materials first gives them a chance to satisfy their curiosity and enables them to focus later.

## Teacher provides materials— ①

Before teaching any hands-on lesson, give each team a chance to play with the materials you will be using. Items such as magnets, leaves, seeds, and rocks can be a source of play, especially when magnifying lenses are provided along with them. Hand-held microscopes are also fascinating to children of all ages.

Depending on the materials available, Cooperative Play can occur within teams simultaneously or by individual teams at a learning center. If the entire class will be playing simultaneously, you'll need a set of materials for each team. Placing the materials at a learning center solves the problem of limited materials since you'll need only enough for one team at a time.

## Students play together– ②

When you introduce the materials to the class, explain any safety guidelines to your children but don't tell them how to play with the objects. Just ask, "What can you learn about these things?" Their play does not have to be "scientific." Children learn simply by handing objects and talking about them with others.

Make sure each team has ample time to play with the materials. If using a learning center, leave the materials out for several days so all students have time to satisfy their curiosity.

• Magnets and materials to test for attraction
• Rock collections and magnifying lenses
• Mirrors and flashlights
• Colored water and eyedroppers
• Homemade musical instruments
• Balance scales and objects to weigh
• Ramps and objects that roll

1. **Teacher Asks Question**

2. **Teacher Announces Corners**

3. **Students Write Choice**

4. **Students Move To Corners**

5. **Students Pair And Discuss Choices**

(See Lesson 10)

In **Corners,** the teacher asks a question with four possible answers and designates a corner of the room for each answer. Each student writes down his or her choice and moves to the corresponding corner. Then the students in each corner pair and discuss their choice.

I like **Corners** for several reasons. In addition to conveying science content, **Corners** gets kids actively mixing with other class members. Students learn that they share interests and opinions with others in the class. **Corners** is especially suitable for primary students because the discussion occurs between pairs of students rather than within teams. Finally, **Corners** is great for perking up the class mood when children have been sitting for a long time.

Your
Cooperative Learning
*Tools*

**① Teacher asks question—**

First, choose your question or topic and identify four different responses. Students can respond to questions, make predictions about experiments, or tell which of four items is a favorite. Below are some sample questions and responses:

*What do you think will happen when the baking soda is added to the vinegar?*
Nothing
The baking soda will float.
The vinegar will change colors.
The vinegar and baking soda will fizz.

*Which animal would you like to study?*
Whale
Dolphin
Shark
Manatee

*What is your favorite season of the* year?
Spring
Summer
Fall
Winter

**② Teacher announces question—**

After stating the question or topic, show your students which corner of the room represents each choice. Post small signs in each corner of the room. Use picture signs with young children.

**③ Students write choice—**

To keep students from changing their minds, have each person write down his or her choice on a piece of scrap paper. Nonwriters can draw a simple picture of their choice.

**④ Students move to corners—**

Ask students to take their written responses and move quietly to the corner they chose.

**⑤ Students pair and discuss choices—**

After all students have moved to corners, have them pair up with a partner. Encourage them to pair up with someone they don't know well rather than choosing their best friends or teammates. Make sure everyone has a partner before telling students what you want them to discuss. You can ask them to give reasons why they made their choice or what they would like to find out about their study topic.

• Making predictions
• Stating preferences
• Answering questions
• Choosing study topics
• Voting for choices
• Expressing opinions

① **Teacher Announces Object or Concept**

② **Students Form Object or Demonstrate Concept**

**(See Lesson 5)**

**Formations** are a fun way to make abstract concepts concrete. Students work as a class or in teams to form an object or demonstrate a concept announced by the teacher. When an entire class works together, class spirit is strengthened. Similarly, team unity is fostered when teammates cooperate to create formations.

Structure **4**
**Formations**

Your
Cooperative Learning
*Tools*

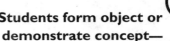

### Teacher announces object or concept—

Think of an object or concept which can be portrayed by the class or individual teams. **Class Formations** involve all members of the class working together on one concept or item. **Team Formations** are created when children work within teams to portray an object or idea.

Many science concepts lend themselves to formations. For instance, students can work together to form a solar system, complete with heavenly bodies revolving around the sun. Students in teams can form a tree, with each member dramatizing a different part. You can have teams portray science inventions or animals being studied.

If each team is going to create a different formation, you can write or draw the items on individual slips of paper. Place the slips in a bag and have one person from each team select a piece of paper without looking.

### Students form object or demonstrate concept—

After you have announced the object or concept you want students to form, let them get to work. Young children may need some guidance at this point. If they have never done this structure before, direct the class through the first **Formation** or choose a team to model one for the class. Coach the team prior to the lesson so they will know what to do and let them demonstrate for the class.

For **Team Formations,** you can supervise each team's practice session by placing the **Formation** activity at a learning center. Let each team rotate to the center during the day to choose their topic and plan how to do their **Formation.** Check with each team while they are there to make sure everyone has an active part in the **Formation.**

Add some excitement to **Team Formations** by having each team present its **Formation** to the class. The rest of the teams put their heads together and try to guess the name of the **Formation.**

• Demonstrating how the seasons are caused
• Creating animals
• Dramatizing inventions
• Demonstrating the action of wind vanes
• Dramatizing the life cycle of an insect
• Making up a food chain or food web
• Demonstrating open and closed circuits
• Demonstrating the water cycle

**①** **Teacher Announces Topic**

**②** **Students Line Up**

**(See Lessons 1 and 11)**

A **Line-Up** is a simple activity in which students physically line up in a specific order. For instance, students can line up according to height, birth date, or number of eyelets on their shoes. **Line-Ups** are ideal for having children sequence pictures, words, or objects. Students can also line up according to their opinion about a certain topic.

One reason I enjoy **Line-Ups** is that these activities provide social as well as academic benefits. **Line-Ups** only take a few minutes to do, but they foster class spirit by allowing children to work with their classmates towards a mutual goal. **Line-Ups** also provide a change of pace when students have been sitting for long periods of time.

Your
Cooperative Learning
*Tools*

### Teacher announces topic— ①

State the topic of your **Line-Up** and explain where in the classroom you want your students to stand. You may want to tape a long string to the floor and place labels at each end. The labels you use will depend on which type of **Line-Up** your class is doing.

One type of **Line-Up** involves having students stand in order according to a personal characteristic such as height or hair length. Be sensitive to your students' feelings as you have them perform this type of activity. Some children are self-conscious about their height or shoe size. Any classbuilding benefits will be lost if children are embarrassed during the **Line-Up.**

Another type of **Line-Up** involves having students place themselves in order according to the characteristics of something they are holding. For instance, each student finds a leaf and the whole class lines up according to leaf length. Pictures of sequential events, such as the stages of an insect life cycle, can be used in **Line-Ups.** If students are given pictures of plants and animals living in a particular habitat, they can line up to form food chains.

A third type of **Line-Up** is often called a **Value Line-Up.** It involves having students get in order according to their opinion about a particular question or topic. For instance, students could respond to the question "Would you like to travel to the moon one day?" Those whose answer is a strong "Yes!" stand at one end of the line. Those who definitely do not want to visit the moon stand at the other end. Students who aren't sure stand somewhere in between.

### Students line up— ②

After announcing the topic, have students line up accordingly. Depending on the difficulty of the topic, you may or may not want to allow students to talk as they place themselves in order. Let the line of students curve around the room so that everyone can see the final sequence.

## Team Line-Ups

In the primary classroom, a full class **Line-Up** may be too challenging at first. You may want to have small groups of students do **Team Line-Ups.** For instance, have each student on a team choose a rock from a collection and tell them to line up from the smoothest rock to the roughest rock. Four rocks are easier than thirty rocks to place in this type of sequence.

## Folded Value Line-Ups

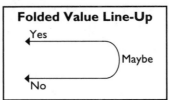

When doing **Value Line-Ups,** it's interesting to have students talk with others about why they responded as they did. One way to do this is to fold the **Line-Up** in half so that students who strongly agree with the statement are paired with those who disagree (see illustration). After folding the **Line-Up,** students discuss their opinions with the person facing them.

**Folded Value Line-Up**

Yes

Maybe

No

• Sequencing words alphabetically
• Sequencing planets according to distance from the sun
• Placing science picture cards in order
• Putting objects in order according to length, weight, or size
• Lining up colors in rainbow sequence
• Responding to questions such as:
• Should people be able to keep wild animals as pets?
• Should people be allowed to burn trash in their yard?

1. **Classmates Mix**

2. **Teacher Announces "Freeze"**

3. **Students Pair**

4. **Teacher Announces Topic**

5. **Pairs Discuss Topic**

**(See Lessons 1, 2, 3 and 6)**

In **Mix-Freeze-Pair,** students move around the room, pair with another classmate, and discuss a question posed by the teacher. In addition to providing a framework for discussion, this structure has classbuilding benefits.  As they interact with others in the class, students are developing important social skills. Because the discussion occurs in pairs, this structure is ideal for primary students. In addition, **Mix-Freeze-Pair** offers a simple change of pace when students have been seated for long periods of time.

## **Classmates mix—** ①
Begin the activity by saying "Mix!" and having students walk quietly around the room.

## **Teacher announces "Freeze"—** ②
After allowing students to mix for about 10 seconds, say "Freeze!" Students immediately stop and stand still.

## **Students pair—** ③
When everyone is still, announce "Pair!" Students pair with the person closest to them and link arms to show that they are partners. Discourage students from intentionally seeking out their best friends; remind them that one reason for doing the activity is to meet other classmates. Establish the rule that students have to find a new partner during each round of **Mix-Freeze-Pair.**

If students can't find a partner, have them move to the front of the room. If several students are left over, they can pair up when they reach this area. If only one person is left, pair with that student yourself or allow three students to form a triad.

## **Teacher announces topic—** ④
Now announce the discussion question or topic. Simple, review-style questions can be used, as well as those aimed at higher level thinking. Examples of possible questions include:

*What objects are attracted to a magnet?*
*Why are rain forests important?*
*How does the sense of hearing help us?*
*How would your life be different without electricity?*

## **Pairs discuss topic—** ⑤
After posing the question, give everyone a few seconds of "think time." Then have pairs discuss their responses. Ask everyone to face you when they have finished discussing the question with their partner. If you want to hear some of the responses, call on a few students to share their ideas with the class. Then say "Mix!" and repeat the activity with additional questions.

- Discussing prior knowledge before a lesson
- Reviewing main ideas at the end of a lesson
- Describing the favorite part of a field trip
- Reviewing science vocabulary
- Stating opinions about science topics
- Discussing predictions before an experiment
- Explaining the results of an experiment
- Answering questions about a chart or graph

① Students Number Off

② Pose Question

③ Heads Together Discussion

④ Choose A Number

⑤ Numbered Students Respond
(See Lessons 4 and 9)

**Numbered Heads Together** is a simple but effective mastery structure. This technique is a fun way to review before an activity or after a lesson. The teacher asks a question, students discuss the answer, and one person on each team responds when their number is called. **Numbered Heads** should be used when recall of basic facts and ideas is desired; the structure is less suitable for questions that have detailed or complex answers.

**Students number off—** ①
Have students number off from 1 - 4 within their teams. To help young children remember their number, make signs for them to wear or place on their desks. Check to make sure everyone knows their number by randomly calling out numbers and having students with that number raise their hands.

**Pose question—** ②
Ask a question that can be answered briefly. For this structure the question should not require a lengthy answer, but rather should have one or more simple answers. For example, "Where does a polar bear live?" or "Name one object attracted to a magnet."

**Heads together discussion—** ③
Team members lean toward the center of the team so that they can quietly discuss the answer. Remind them that anyone could be called on so they need to make sure all teammates know at least one correct answer. When everyone on a team knows the answer they sit back in their seats and stop talking.

Your
Cooperative Learning
*Tools*

**④**

## Choose a number—

When everyone has stopped talking, select a student from each team by choosing a number from 1 - 4. I like to use a spinner to select a number; spinning for a number creates a game-like atmosphere.  (Several spinners for the overhead projector are available from *Kagan Publishing*).

**⑤**

## Numbered students respond—

### Finger Response
Depending on the type of answer, the numbered student may respond in many ways. If a numerical answer is needed, have each person hold up the correct number of fingers. If a one word answer is required, let them give a choral response when you give a signal.

### Team Chalkboard
My favorite response method is team chalkboards. I provide each team with a small chalkboard, a piece of chalk, and a sock for an eraser. The numbered student writes or draws the team answer on the board and turns it face down. On a signal from me, team chalkboards are held up for me to check.

### Laminated Posterboard
If you don't have individual chalkboards, you can laminate a 10" x 12" piece of posterboard for each team. Distribute an overhead projector pen and a damp paper towel to each team also. Or you can also divide the class chalkboard into sections and have the designated students come forward and write the team's answer in the space provided.

### Response Cards
Young children enjoy holding up prepared response cards. Make each team a set of response cards from large index cards. Write or draw all possible answers on individual cards. For instance, when reviewing the parts of a flower write each vocabulary word or sketch each flower part on a separate card.

When you call out the question students may handle the response cards as they discuss the answer. However, before the student number is called all cards must be shuffled and spread out randomly in the center of the team. Students may not stack the cards with the answer on top.

### Individual Accountability
No matter what response mode you choose, make sure students don't help each other after a number is announced. Individual accountability is important. If students know that they will not be able to receive help if called upon, they will be more likely to listen when their team is discussing the answer.

After completing one round of **Numbered Heads,** continue to pose questions as needed. Try to allow all students the opportunity to answer at least one question.

## Substitute Colors or Shapes for Numbers

Instead of assigning numbers, assign each team member one of four different shapes or colors. Place a small color or shape tag on each student's desk. Instead of choosing a numbered student to respond, name a color or shape. For instance, "All greens show me the correct number with your fingers." Or "If you are an oval, write the team's answer on the chalkboard."

## Individuals Think / Numbered Heads Together

To increase student involvement and improve the quality of responses, give students think time before the team discussion. Immediately after posing the question, allow 10 or 15 seconds for each person to think of his or her own answer before allowing anyone to speak.

## Individuals Write / Numbered Heads Together

To ensure even more individual participation, add in another step. Immediately after posing the question, have each person think of their own answer and write it on a slip of scrap paper. The team discussion may only begin after everyone has an idea down on paper.

• Reviewing science vocabulary
• Identifying common objects (rocks, flowers, seeds, etc.)
• Naming ways animals are adapted to their environment
• Reviewing science safety rules
• Identifying parts of a flower

① **Teacher Designates Pairs**

② **Teacher Assigns Task**

③ **Pairs Complete Task**

(See Lessons 3, 4, 5, 6, 7, 8, 10, 11, and 12)

**Pairs** is the simplest of all structures; two students work together to complete an assigned task. **Pairs** is particularly well suited to the primary classroom. Minimal social skills are needed for two students to work together. Both are likely to be equally involved with the task. Taking turns is easier in pairs than in teams.

Pair work is also important in science because it allows greater hands-on contact with science materials. Furthermore, this structure is helpful when two sets of hands are needed to hold materials together during an activity.

The best aspect of **Pairs** is that working with a partner is fun! The magic of science doubles when students are able to share the experience with a friend.

Your
Cooperative Learning
*Tools*

**Teacher designates pairs—**

If your students are seated in teams
of four, you can form your pairs
easily by splitting the team into two
sets of partners. Keep in mind the
ability levels of your students. Don't
place two students together who are
both likely to struggle with the task.
If your students are not seated in
teams, you can assign partners
in advance.

① 

**Teacher assigns task—**

② 

Assign the task to your students and explain the
procedure. For example, students can work together
to build weather instruments or to perform an
experiment. Give clear, concise directions, explaining
how they are to share the work. If possible, assign
roles so that each person has a specific job to do.

Tell students to ask their partner if they have a
question. If neither of them knows the answer, they
both raise their hands to signal a pair question.

**Pairs complete task—**

③ 

While your pairs are working,
monitor their progress carefully.
Make sure that they are
participating equally. Encourage
interdependence by answering
questions only when both hands
are raised.

- Constructing musical instruments
- Completing a survey
- Experimenting with batteries and bulbs
- Designing a paper airplane
- Graphing the results of an experiment
- Classifying rocks
- Making a kaleidoscope
- Investigating magnets
- Conducting an experiment
- Testing reflexes
- Collecting insects or leaves

1. **Students Number Off**

2. **Question Or Topic Is Posed**

3. **Students Take Turns Sharing A Response**

   **(See Lessons 2, 3, 7, 8, 10, 11, and 12)**

**RoundRobin** is one of the most simple and versatile of all cooperative learning structures. It allows students to take turns sharing ideas, answering questions, stating observations, or making predictions. In **RoundRobin**, students do not discuss or evaluate each other's responses, they simply listen to each other.

Your
Cooperative Learning
*Tools*

**Students number off—** ①

Within each team, students number off in order. For young children, assign numbers and give them numbered tags to wear or place on their desks.

**Question or topic is posed—** ②

As the teacher, you will pose the topic or question. For example, you might ask them to name objects that are attracted to a magnet. Or you might ask them to share their predictions just before performing a science experiment. Sometimes you will allow them time to freely explore a set of materials and **RoundRobin** their observations.

**RoundRobin** can also be used at the beginning of a class period to stimulate interest in the upcoming lesson or to review a concept. Similarly, it can be used at the end of a lesson to provide closure.

**Students take turns sharing a response—** ③

After you pose the question, designate someone by number to begin sharing their response. After that person has answered, the next numbered person on each team responds until everyone has shared an answer. Be sure students know whether they are expected to stop after everyone has responded, or if they should continue until they run out of ideas. Encourage students to practice active listening skills by leaning forward, making eye contact, and focusing on what each person is saying.

## RallyRobin

In **RallyRobin**, students form pairs within the team and take turns sharing ideas back and forth. This calls for more active participation, since students are speaking 50% of the time.

## Team RoundRobin

For a **Team RoundRobin**, the class forms a large circle with teams clustered together. In turn, each team responds to a topic or reports the results of an activity. Sometimes a representative is chosen from each team

to share their team's findings. This variation provides an excellent way for teams to report the results of a science experiment to the entire class.

## Class RoundRobin

**Class RoundRobin** is often called Circle Time or Community Circle. Class members form a large circle and take turns sharing ideas. This variation is ideal for the primary classroom, especially when introducing active listening skills. Class Roundrobin also exposes children to many different ideas and ways of thinking.

- Stating observations
- Making predictions
- Sharing opinions
- Asking questions
- Naming zoo animals
- Naming parts of a plant or types of plants
- Naming parts of the body
- Naming types of weather
- Naming animals in a particular climate region
- Naming weather instruments
- Naming planets and other heavenly bodies

① **Students Number Off**

② **Teacher Explains Task**

③ **Students Take Turns Completing Task**

(See Lessons 2, 3, 5, 6, 7, 9, and 11)

**RoundTable** is a flexible and adaptable structure. Basically, **RoundTable** provides a method for taking turns within teams. This structure is similar to **RoundRobin** except that students are completing a task rather than just verbally sharing responses. Often, **RoundTable** involves passing a sheet of paper around and taking turns writing responses. In science, however, **RoundTable** may also be used when science materials are shared among students on a team. For example, you can give each person a hand lens and one object to view. As they finish viewing their object, they pass the object to the next person on the team.

My favorite way to use **RoundTable** in science is for sorting objects such as leaves, rocks, or seeds. One person "deals out" the items to be sorted so that everyone has approximately the same number. Then everyone takes turns placing their items into category piles in the center of the team. Pictures of animals or plants can also be sorted this way.

**RallyTable,** a variation of **RoundTable,** is often used in the early grades since it involves pairs rather than teams.

Structure **10**
**RoundTable/
RallyTable**

Your
Cooperative Learning
***Tools***

**Students number off—** ①
Have your students number off in order within their teams. For young children, assign numbers and give them numbered tags to wear or place on desks.

**Teacher explains task—** ②
Begin **RoundTable** by explaining the task you want your students to take turns completing. If the task involves written responses, explain how to pass the paper around the team.

If the task involves doing an activity, explain the procedure for carrying out the task. For instance, if students are going to take turns using a pan balance to weigh objects, demonstrate the procedure as everyone watches.

**Students take turns
completing task—** ③
After you have explained the task, designate a person on each team to begin the activity. Everyone else offers praise and encouragement as they carefully watch. When the first person finishes, he or she passes the materials to the next person on the team. Everyone continues taking turns and passing materials until the activity has been completed.

## RallyTable

**RallyTable** increases participation by breaking the team into two sets of pairs. One paper is given to each pair, and they pass the paper back and forth as they complete the activity. **RallyTable** is also useful for having two people share science materials. This structure is ideal for the primary classroom because it's easier to take turns in pairs. Young children often don't have the patience to wait for three other people to complete their part of an activity. With **RallyTable**, students are able to actively manipulate materials a greater percentage of the time.

## Simultaneous Roundtable

Normally in **RoundTable** only one person is working at a time. In **Simultaneous RoundTable**, however, everyone has a task to complete simultaneously. If the task involves writing, everyone needs a piece of paper and a pencil. For example, Person #1 may have a paper entitled "Fish," Person #2 may have a paper labeled "Amphibians," Person #3 may have "Birds," and Person #4 may have "Mammals." When the signal is given, each person writes one example of their topic. After they write a word, they pass their papers clockwise. Each time they receive a paper they add to the list.

- Listing names of animals
- Listing types of plants
- Writing observations
- Testing magnets
- Sharing microscopes
- Completing charts
- Sorting objects into categories
- Weighing and measuring items

(1) **Students Create Problems**

(2) **Teams Send Problems To Other Teams**

(3) **Team Members Work Problems**

(4) **Teams Continue Sending And Working Problems**

**(See Lessons 2 and 3)**

**Send-A-Problem** turns a problem-solving session into a game. By creating problems and sending them to other students, teams experience the fun of challenging others to solve their problems.

The "problems" used in this structure don't have to be stated in written form. **Send-A-Problem** has hands-on applications in science. Students can send each other objects to be identified, measured, or viewed under a microscope. They can also send each other classification schemes to be deciphered or science mysteries to be solved. Don't be afraid to apply this structure creatively!

This is an advanced structure for primary students, but it can be adapted and used in a simpler form with young children. Since some classes may be ready for the original version, I have decided to write up the full version with the primary version listed as a variation.

**Students create problems—** (1)

Students will create their own problems for this activity. For instance, children can write review questions after a science lesson. Each person writes one question on the front of an index card and the answer on the back. To make sure each problem is stated clearly and its answer is correct, team members should check each other's cards.

In cases where objects instead of written problems are sent, ask students to label each object clearly and provide answer keys on index cards. Then have them place all objects and answer keys on a paper plate or tray.

## (2) Teams send problems to other teams—

Have students number off from 1–4 within their teams. To help young children remember their numbers, make numbered role cards for them to wear or place on their desks.

Since each team will be sending its problems to another team, decide the classroom rotation pattern in advance. Begin by having Person #4 deliver their team's problems to Person #1 on the next team. For simplicity's sake, at the end of each round Person #4 will deliver the problems to Person #1 on the next team.

## (3) Team members work problems—

When the set of problems arrives, person #1 keeps all the index cards in hand. He or she becomes the "teacher" for this round and reads the first question aloud. Everyone else is a "student" and solves the problem individually. After everyone writes their answer, they compare and discuss their solutions. The "teacher" then checks the team's answer by looking on the back of the index card. If the entire team disagrees with the answer on the back of the card, they send a messenger to the original team to get clarification.

Next, the "teacher" hand the entire stack of problem cards to Person #2. That person becomes the "teacher" for the next problem and follows the same steps outlined above. All four problems should be solved in the same manner, with a new "teacher" designated for each problem.

## (4) Teams continue sending and working problems—

When all four problems have been solved, Person #4 takes the stack to Person #1 on the next team. If problems pile up because one team works more slowly than the others, you may want to set a time limit for each round.

### Primary Send-A-Problem

In the primary grades most children are not ready to make up their own problems. If this is true for your class, you can create the problems for your students to solve. Write the problems on individual slips of paper or numbered index cards. Illustrate the problems with simple sketches for students with limited reading abilities. Provide each team with an answer key.

Another way to simplify this structure is by limiting the number of objects or problems being sent from team to team. Sending only one or two objects eliminates the somewhat confusing within-team rotation described in Step Three of the full version.

Another modification involves using the role titles of "Sender" and "Receiver" instead of having students number off. Make role card signs for the "Sender" and "Receiver" on each team. This way students will know who is supposed to pass the object or problem card to whom.

• Writing descriptions of rocks or leaves to challenge other teams
• Solving brainteasers
• Writing questions about a graph of experiment results
• Writing questions about information that has been read aloud
• Measuring the volume of a selection of containers
• Solving science-related math word problems
• Playing with science toys

① **Teacher Assigns Topic**

② **Teammates Discuss Topic**

(See Lessons 4 and 9)

**Team Discussion** is a structure which can be slipped into almost any lesson. The teacher assigns a topic and team members talk about it. **Team Discussions** are useful when introducing a topic; you can have students discuss what they already know to get them interested in learning something new. During the lesson itself, teams can discuss ways to solve a problem or how they feel about a topic. **Team Discussions** can also be used for review at the end of a lesson.

**Team Discussion** is a very versatile structure, but its use must be monitored carefully. One problem with **Team Discussions** is that children may not participate equally. Some children will do all the talking and others may not contribute anything to the discussion. In this case, break the team into pairs for a **Pair Discussion**, or try a different structure like **RoundRobin** or **Think-Pair-Share**.

Another problem involves the possibility that students may reinforce each other's inaccurate science ideas during **Team Discussions**. As you listen to children discuss a topic in teams, you'll often hear them accepting incorrect science information as fact. For this reason, **Team Discussions** in the primary classroom should often be followed by a **Class Discussion** to clear up misunderstandings.

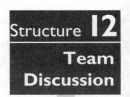

Your
Cooperative Learning
*Tools*

**①**

**Teacher assigns topic—**
The best topics for **Team Discussions** are low-consensus questions. Instead of questions like "What is the name of this leaf?" which have just one answer, try questions like "What are some ways that your leaves are alike and different?"

**②**

**Teammates discuss topic—**
After the topic is announced, teammates put their heads together to discuss the topic. You may want to assign a time limit so that everyone knows just how much time they have to discuss the topic.

While your students are involved in their discussions, be sure to monitor your teams carefully. Especially at first, some teams may drift away from the assigned topic and need redirection. As you walk, listen to what your students are saying. You may discover that they don't understand the question or that students don't have enough background knowledge to discuss the topic.

• Can water look clean and be polluted? How?
• What simple machines can you see in this room?
• What are some examples of seeds that people eat?
• In what ways are plants different from animals?
• Why are fish shaped the way they are?
• What are some reasons that animals are endangered?
• What is a mammal?
• What can we do to keep from making so much trash?

**Pair Discussion**
To encourage greater involvement, you may want to divide each team in half and involve the members in **Pair Discussions**. Younger children may find **Pair Discussions** easier than **Team Discussions**.

**Class Discussion**
Sometimes a **Class Discussion** is needed to allow all members to contribute ideas or to clear up misunderstandings. However, **Class Discussions** should be limited since they are a very weak form of cooperative learning.

① **Students Number Off**

② **Teacher Explains Topic**

③ **Teammates Interview Each Other In Turn**

(See Lesson 8)

**Team Interview** is a simple structure for sharing information. Teammates interview each other in turn about a topic stated by the teacher. **Team Interview** can be used for giving science book reports, sharing the results of a home activity, or answering questions about personal preferences. When **Team Interview** takes the form of a guessing game, it encourages logical thinking skills.

# Team Interview

Your
Cooperative Learning
*Tools*

## ① Students number off—

Have students number off in order within teams. For young children, assign numbers and give them numbered tags to wear or place on their desks.

## ② Teacher explains topic—

Explain the interview topic to the class and tell students how much time they will have for each interview. One minute per interview is generally sufficient.

**Team Interview** is ideal for having students report about their favorite science book. Let each student have his or her book in hand during the interview. You can also use this structure for reporting the results of a homework assignment or activity.

If your students have not used **Team Interview** before, model the structure for them by pretending to be the "interviewee." Ask them what kinds of questions they could ask to find out about the book or report being shared. List their questions on the board. Modeling is essential when introducing this structure to young children. In addition, each time you use **Team Interview** you'll find it helpful to let students brainstorm possible questions before they begin.

**Team Interview** can also take the form of a game. The student being interviewed thinks of a mystery number, word, object, or animal. Other students on the team ask questions until they can guess the mystery item. For instance, the interviewee might secretly choose an animal from a stack of endangered wildlife game cards. To help them identify the animal, the others ask questions like "Does your animal fly?" or "Where does your animal live?"

## ③ Teammates interview each other in turn—

After explaining the topic and brainstorming possible questions, designate one person on each team to begin. Call a number and have students with that number stand. Their teammates become interviewers and take turns asking them questions. It's best to have team members **RoundRobin** their questions so that everyone is equally involved.

Give a signal after one minute or the time allotted for the first interview. The signal could be verbal or an action such as ringing a bell. On the signal, the person being interviewed sits down and the next numbered person stands up. It's important to have the person being interviewed stand. This management technique allows you to see who is being interviewed at any time. It also helps keep the questions directed to the proper person so the interview doesn't turn into a discussion. Continue until everyone has been interviewed.

• Sharing science book reports
• Guessing a mystery object or sound
• Answering questions about a science "show and tell" item
• Reporting the results of an experiment completed at home

**①** **Teacher Explains Project**

**②** **Teacher Assigns Roles**

**③** **Teams Complete Project**

**④** **Teams Present project**

**(See Lessons 1, 4, 6, 8, 9, 11, and 12)**

**Team Projects** involve the creation of a unique product by each team, and can be very simple or very involved. They may be relatively unstructured or highly structured, depending on the individual requirements of the project. **Team Projects** may take as little as five minutes or as long as several weeks to complete. I like **Team Projects** because in addition to their usefulness academically, they build team spirit. Team members take pride in the results of their work together.

**Team Projects** have a variety of uses in science. For example, teams may create posters showing food webs or illustrating the bones of the body. Teams can create their own rock, leaf, or seed collections. This structure is ideal for having students create team booklets. I have also discovered that **Team Projects** are useful when students work together to complete science experiments and investigations.

---

**Teacher explains project—** **①**

When you assign a **Team Project**, be sure to explain the project clearly to your students. Decide in advance the basic guidelines, but be flexible to your students' input. Make sure you tell the class the amount of time you are allowing for them to complete their project.

---

**②**

### Teacher assigns roles—

Assigning roles is one of the best ways to equalize participation. When you decide on the roles your students will need, keep in mind the purposes of the project, the number of students on each team, and the ages of your students. If you have four people on each team, you need four roles. If one team has five people, be sure to create another role for the fifth person on that team (if only Praiser or Encourager). The following roles are appropriate for many science activities:

| Role | Description |
|---|---|
| *Lead Scientist* | Keeps the group on task. Makes sure everyone follows directions. |
| *Materials Monitor* | Gets all the materials for the team. |
| *Cleanup Captain* | Makes sure that everyone helps clean up and makes sure the area is left neat. |
| *Time Keeper* | Keeps time for the group. |
| *Quiet Captain* | Monitors noise level. |
| *Praiser* | Praises the accomplishments of team members. |
| *Recorder* | Records the ideas of the team. |
| *Reporter* | Reports the team's ideas to the class. |
| *Question Commander* | Is the only one who may ask the teacher questions, and only after checking to see that no one on the team knows the answer. |

You may also want to make up roles which are appropriate only for a particular activity. For instance, the "Catch a Rainbow" lesson calls for Rainbow Makers and Rainbow Catchers.

The easiest way to assign roles is by number. Have your students number off 1 - 4 and announce the role assignments by number. Make role cards to help everyone remember their roles. For each student, fold stiff paper into a "tent" and write the name of their role on both sides. You can also make one-sided role cards which can be hung from a string around each child's neck or pinned on each shirt. If you decide to rotate roles during the activity, have students switch their role cards.

I have developed an easy way to ensure that roles are rotated fairly. Construct a Rotating Role Finder with the pattern provided. Write your four roles in the spaces on the outside circle. After the device is made, simply turn the inside circle to assign new roles.

Rotating roles gives everyone a chance to perform all tasks, but the practice of switching roles can be confusing and distracting. For simple projects, you will probably want each student to keep the same role throughout the activity.

**③**

### Teams complete project—

After explaining the project, distribute materials and let students get to work. If close supervision is needed with an activity, have students complete the project at a learning center. Monitor the center yourself or solicit the help of a parent volunteer.

**④**

### Teams present project—

Allow some time for students to share their work with others. Providing this time shows students that you value their efforts. Teams may present to other teams or to the entire class. Teams can share the results of an experiment by taking part in the creation of a class graph.

- Creating collections of rocks, leaves, seeds, etc.
- Designing posters of seasons, biomes, types of weather
- Creating collages of mammals, birds, reptiles, etc.
- Illustrating food webs of various habitats
- Developing the best paper helicopter to enter in a contest
- Creating a musical instrument from ordinary materials
- Experimenting with plants or seeds
- Making team booklets
- Creating simple weather instruments

# Planning Team Projects

**Team Projects** are unlike other structures because each project is unique. The steps for completing each project are different and depend entirely on a particular project's desired outcome or "product." To achieve this outcome, **Team Projects** may incorporate other structures. Yet some products are highly creative, and a lack of structure may be needed during this creation process.

All of these factors open up the possibility of unequal participation. For this reason, keep in mind the Four Basic Principles of cooperative learning when you plan your projects. Decide in advance how you will incorporate positive interdependence, equal participation, individual accountability, and simultaneity. Since each project is unique, the manner in which you do so will vary from project to project.

Planning a **Team Project** to incorporate the Four Basic Principles is challenging, especially at first. However, without this type of planning cooperative learning disintegrates into "groupwork." Some students take over and do everything, while others are free to do nothing. Positive interdependence, individual accountability, equal participation, and simultaneity are essential in **Team Projects.**

**Positive interdependence** is present when all students must participate in order for a project to be completed successfully. One way to make students interdependent is to limit the materials and assign one material to each person. For example, put one person in charge of the scissors, assign the glue to another, and give the remaining students the markers. Another way to make students dependent upon each other is to give each person only part of the information needed to complete the project. Finally, I like to assign roles so that each person has a specific job.

Assigning roles also helps ensure **equal participation.** Plan carefully to make sure the tasks are divided and assigned so that no one ends up doing all the work. If some roles involve more participation than others, rotate roles throughout the project. Using other structures within the **Team Project** is another way to encourage equal participation. I often have my students use **RoundTable** and **RoundRobin** when they are doing **Team Projects.**

**Individual accountability** is needed to make sure that each person actually participates in the final project. Having students color-code projects such as posters can help you see how much each person has contributed. If each person is assigned a different color marker or paper, you can assess participation with a quick glance. If no obvious method of determining accountability exists, monitor your students carefully while they work. Spend a little time talking with individual students on each team to find out how they participated and what they learned from the activity.

Finally, when planning a **Team Project** be sure to consider the principle of **simultaneity.** Cooperative learning is in its weakest form when three people are watching one person complete a task. Try to structure the activity so that everyone is doing something at the same time. One way to increase simultaneity is to use pair work within the confines of the **Team Projects.** Another way is to plan the project so that everyone works on one part simultaneously and then assembles the completed project at the end.

**Rotating Role Finder Directions—**

1. Photocopy this page on colored paper and laminate, if possible.

2. Cut out base and numbered dial on dark lines.

3. Write one role title on each of the four outer sections of the base.

4. Center the numbered dial on top of the base.

5. Push a paper fastener through the center of both circles.

6. Turn numbered dial to rotate roles.

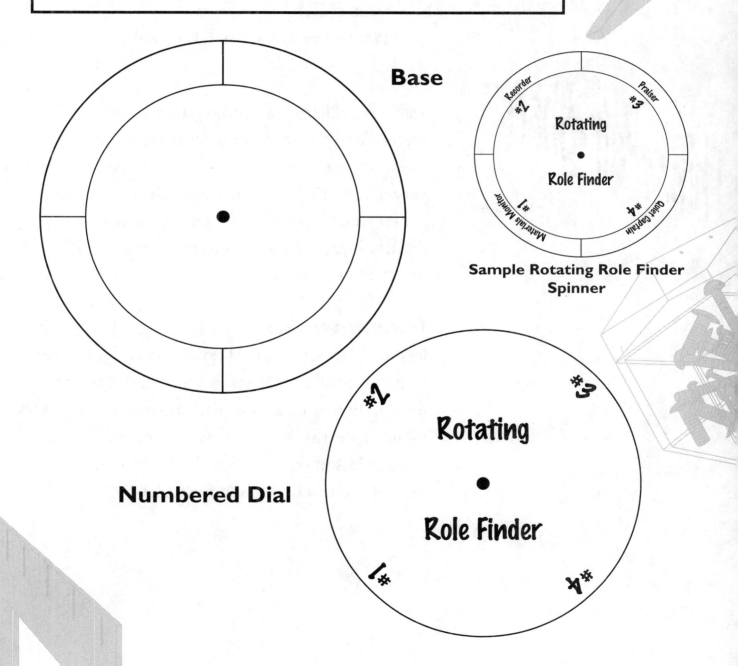

**Base**

**Sample Rotating Role Finder Spinner**

**Numbered Dial**

① Teacher Poses Question

② Individuals Think

③ Pairs Discuss Responses

④ Students Share Responses With Class

(See Lessons 2, 3, 4, 5, 6, 7, 8, 10, and 12)

**Think-Pair-Share** is a simple yet powerful structure. Instead of a few students answering the teacher's question, everyone in the class must respond. By its very nature, the structure demands involvement. When students know they will be expected to discuss a question or a concept, they are motivated to pay attention.

**Think-Pair-Share** can be used during any part of the lesson. Discussing prior knowledge is a great way to involve students from the very start. During the lesson, discussing a topic with a partner encourages higher-level thinking and gives students time to process lesson content. Finally, the structure can be used at the end of a lesson for review.

Your
Cooperative Learning
*Tools*

### ① Teacher poses question—

Begin by asking a question related to the lesson. Questions which stimulate discussion are best, as opposed to those with a single, simple answer. For example, when reading science literature you can ask students to predict what will happen next or discuss whether they agree with a character's behavior. **Think-Pair-Share** is also ideal for having students making predictions before an experiment or discussing results after the activity.

### ② Individuals think—

Provide think time before allowing students to discuss their answers. This is a critical step, since a student who does not have time to develop a personal response will have nothing to contribute to the pair discussion. You might even ask everyone to give you a thumbs up signal when they are ready.

### ③ Pairs discuss responses—

Now ask students to pair with a partner to discuss their ideas. You should designate partners in advance so time is not wasted deciding who will speak with whom. Monitor this step carefully. Walk around the room and listen to what the children are saying to each other. Sometimes you'll hear comments that indicate a concept was misunderstood. Occasionally you'll find a pair who are completely off the topic and need some redirection.

### ④ Students share responses with class—

Randomly call on students to share their responses. This part of the structure is very important for clearing up misunderstandings or focusing attention on a particular issue. To hold students accountable for listening to each other, ask them to only share what their partner said during the discussion. Students need to know that a discussion involves both speaking and listening.

- Making predictions
- Making inferences
- Discussing observations
- Drawing conclusions
- Explaining how to separate plastics for recycling
- Naming some effects of air pollution on health
- Explaining how a particular animal is adapted to its environment
- Telling the favorite part of a field trip
- Answering questions about science literature
- Describing weather instruments
- Explaining why rainforests are important

### Think-Pair-Square

Sometimes you'll use the structure simply to stimulate thought or provoke a discussion. In this case, you may not need students to share their answers with the class. In **Think-Pair-Square**, students think about their responses, pair to discuss them, and then discuss their answers as a team. In the last step they "square" their responses rather than sharing them with the class.

### Think-Write-Pair-Share

If some students seem to have nothing to say during the pair discussion, have everyone jot down their ideas before speaking. Students are more likely to become involved in a discussion after they have committed their ideas to paper. Nonwriters can use inventive spelling or sketch their ideas in picture form.

STRUCTURE VARIATIONS STRUCTURE VARIATIONS

**Child-Centered Science** ◆
**Science Process Skills** ◆
**Science Journals** ◆
**Curriculum Links** ◆
**Literature Connections** ◆
**Science Materials** ◆
**Safety Spotlight** ◆
**Science Lesson Format** ◆
**Ready...Set...Science!** ◆

## Child-Centered Science

As my lesson ideas began taking shape, I spent hours reviewing the science resources available to primary teachers. I discovered that many science activity books were overwhelmingly teacher-centered. That is, the activities were designed more for the convenience of the teacher than with any real understanding of the way children learn. Most "science" activities involved coloring pictures or cutting and pasting items on a worksheet. The more I read, the more determined I became that my lessons would offer an alternative to this pseudo-science.

As a result, *Wee Science* lessons are child-centered. I recognize that young children are not simply little adults; the manner in which children learn is significantly different from the way older students learn. The National Association of Elementary School Principals recently released a guidebook of quality indicators for early childhood programs. To quote *Early Childhood Education and the Elementary Principal,* "Young children acquire knowledge by manipulating, exploring, and experimenting with real objects. They learn almost exclusively by doing, and through movement." (NAESP, 1990)

# Child-Centered Science

| Characteristics of Young Children | Implications for Science Education |
|---|---|
| Children learn best by involving all their senses | • Plan activities which require children to use their senses of taste, touch, smell, hearing, and sight. |
| Children learn best by actively exploring and handling real objects | • When possible, use real objects instead of worksheets and pictures.<br>• Provide time for students to explore and discover their world.<br>• Provide a safe environment for exploration.<br>• Set up a science learning center. |
| Children's writing skills are limited initially but develop rapidly | • Provide opportunities for children to write and record ideas.<br>• Accept "inventive" spelling.<br>• Allow students to draw pictures when recording ideas or data.<br>• Encourage the use of science journals. |
| Children learn through play | • Allow time for Cooperative Play with manipulatives before explaining how to use the items in a lesson. |
| Children generally have short attention spans | • Plan a variety of short activities rather than a single long one.<br>• Keep children actively involved instead of in their seats for long periods. |
| Children have difficulty remembering a list of directions | • Give directions one step at a time.<br>• Post a list of directions which use pictures and key words to summarize the steps. |

# Child-Centered Science (continued)

| Characteristics of Young Children | Implications for Science Education |
|---|---|
| Children are naturally curious, always wanting to know why and how | • Encourage children's questions.<br>• When possible, lead children to discover their own answers.<br>• Ask questions yourself. |
| Children often have difficulty learning to share and take turns in a group setting | • Have children work in pairs before progressing to larger teams.<br>• Use modeling and role play to teach social skills.<br>• Spend a few moments reflecting on social skills after each cooperative activity. |
| Children love to talk about their discoveries and share their new knowledge | • Place children in cooperative groups for science activities.<br>• Talk one-on-one with your students about what they are learning.<br>• Encourage your students to use science works they have learned. |
| Children need to experience success | • Emphasize process rather than product.<br>• Don't expect perfection.<br>• Consider students' developmental levels when planning lessons.<br>• Provide a warm, caring environment. |
| Children learn through repeated exposure to concepts | • Allow children to repeat activities throughout the year.<br>• Place materials in a learning center for children to practice skills they learned earlier. |
| Children enjoy initiating some of their own learning activities | • Provide time for Cooperative Play with materials.<br>• Incorporate children's suggestions into your science lessons.<br>• Keep a variety of science materials available for independent student use. |

As I consulted with other elementary teachers and observed primary classes, I compiled a list of characteristics of young children. I reflected upon each characteristic and its implications for science education in the early grades. Eventually, I organized these ideas into the chart which accompanies this text.

Cooperative process science combines cooperative learning techniques, process skill instruction, and an appreciation for the needs of young children. As I wrote each science lesson, I considered the unique way young children learn. Every single lesson puts real objects into the hands of every child. Children have an opportunity to play with those manipulatives before using them in a lesson. Worksheets are included, but only as a supplement to the hands-on activities.

## Science Process Skills

Even in the early grades, children need to develop process skills by doing science actively. Recent curriculum reforms place as much emphasis on process skills as on content. Furthermore, many states are developing performance-based science tests for students. These tests involve sending students through a series of stations containing hands-on tasks. Obviously students will not be successful at these types of tasks unless they have frequent opportunities to use process skills in the classroom.

Exactly what science process skills should we teach? Consult a dozen different resources, and you'll find a dozen different process skill lists.

I have selected ten skills that range from the simple to the complex. An overview of these skills will help you understand their importance. Each process skill is designated by an icon.

### Observing

Observation skills are essential to science. Before students can identify, classify, or infer, they must be able to use all their senses to observe their world. In addition to seeing objects and events, students must taste, touch, smell, and listen to their environment.

*Examples of observation activities include:*
*Tasting rain forest foods*
*Touching feathers, fur, and scales*
*Smelling the air after a hard rain*
*Listening to the sounds of the forest*

### Identifying

Identification involves labeling objects and events. Naming objects often enables us to discuss those objects more easily. However, be careful not to require students to memorize names purely for the sake of memorization. Students often enjoy being able to identify local trees, rocks, and insects, but that enjoyment can easily be destroyed if students must memorize names without the opportunity to handle concrete objects.

*Examples of identification activities include:*
*Labeling rock and mineral collections*
*Identifying leaves, seeds, and trees*
*Naming the bones of the body*
*Naming the parts of a plant*

## Classifying

As students develop their observation skills, they begin to notice similarities and differences between objects. They begin to sort and group objects based on their observations. You can foster these skills by teaching them various methods of classification, such as Venn diagrams or dichotomous sorting "trees."

*For example:*
*Sorting seeds or leaves*
*Classifying animals according to body characteristics*
*Sorting recyclable trash by category*

## Predicting

Prediction involves making an educated guess about what will happen before an event takes place. When students perform experiments, making a prediction is often called "making a hypothesis." Prediction is a valuable skill for students to develop because it involves applying previously learned science concepts to new situations. Students become more involved in the outcome of a science activity when they are first given time to predict what will happen.

*Some examples of prediction activities include:*
*Making a hypothesis before an experiment*
*Predicting the ending of a story*
*Predicting the weather based on observations*

## Making Models

Many science concepts involve objects so large or complex that students have a difficult time understanding them. Often these concepts can be simplified by constructing models. For instance, a thermometer may seem to be a magical instrument to many students. By making one from a bottle and a straw, students can begin to understand how a thermometer works.

*Other simple models include:*
*Paper airplanes for studying flight*
*A hard-boiled egg to represent the earth*
*Homemade weather instruments*
*Musical instruments made from simple materials*

## Measuring

One of the most basic science skills students need is competence in measurement. Since the international standard for measurement in science is the Metric system, the lessons in this book involve metric measurement. Students who take performance-based science tests are expected to have a working knowledge of the Metric system; hands-on practice with these skills is essential.

*Examples of activities which involve measurement include:*
*Weighing a rock*
*Measuring the distance a paper airplane flew*
*Measuring air temperature*

## Organizing Data

When students do experiments, they often collect data. We can easily teach students to organize the information they collect by providing charts and graphs for them to use. Eventually, we can teach them to make their own charts and graphs. Primary children need to begin by making graphs with real objects, such as leaves or seeds. Later they can graph pictures of objects.

*Activities which involve organizing data include:*
*Graphing favorite foods of classmates*
*Recording experiment results on a chart*
*Graphing temperatures*

## Inferring

Students have truly mastered a science concept when they can make inferences based on what they have learned. Providing plenty of opportunity for kids to "figure things out" on their own will develop the skill of inferring. Even when students don't make correct inferences, praise them for their attempts to figure things out independently.

*Examples of activities which involve inferences include:*
*Inferring that popcorn burned by smelling it*
*Drawing conclusions about the results of an experiment*
*Figuring out why a classroom plant may have died*

## Experimenting

Experimentation integrates many other process skills. Unfortunately, the term "experimenting" is often used loosely. Many people believe that any science activity is an "experiment." However, a true experiment has several identifiable characteristics.

Generally an experiment is conducted in order to answer a question, such as "Do seeds need sunlight to sprout?" Many times the person conducting the experiment makes a *hypothesis,* or an educated guess, about the outcome of the experiment. The scientist follows a specific series of steps, called the *procedure,* in order to answer the question. Throughout the experiment, the scientist attempts to control *variables.* This simply means that he or she tries to keep most parts of the experiment the same, only changing the one part being tested. Scientists also conduct repeated *trials;* in other words, they repeat their experiments to eliminate the chance that their results were due to error. As scientists experiment, they record *data* such as observations or measurements. They organize their data with charts or graphs and state *conclusions* based on their results.

Even in the early grades, we can help students understand the process of experimentation. First, we can have them make predictions before they experiment. We can also discuss the importance of changing only one part of the experiment at a time. By having students conduct repeated trials, they learn the importance of not drawing conclusions based on one set of data.

Finally, we can teach students to organize their data so that they are able to draw conclusions about their experiments.

Children can perform many simple experiments in the classroom and at home.

*Some examples of experiment questions include:*
*Which brand of popcorn pops the most?*
*What kind of food does my cat like best?*
*Which battery lasts the longest?*

## Communicating

Communication skills encompass speaking, writing, reading, and listening. With cooperative learning, many of these skills are integrated automatically. In every lesson, students must communicate their ideas effectively to their teammates or the team will be unable to function.

*Specific activities to improve*
*communication skills include:*
*Writing in a science journal*
*Listening to science literature*
*Reporting the results of an experiment*

## Science Journals

One communication skill often overlooked in science is writing. When students are working in teams, it's especially important to have them reflect in writing upon what they have learned. If we don't integrate writing into our lessons, we may find that students are enjoying science immensely without retaining any concepts. Writing about science makes it not only hands-on but *minds-on.*

An excellent way to encourage writing is to have students keep a Science Journal. Students can use their journals for listing new words, telling about an experiment, writing how they felt about an activity, or drawing something they learned.  For your convenience, I included "Science Journal Suggestions" at the end of every lesson. Look for the Science Journal icon to find these suggestions.

You can have students create journals in a number of different ways. One easy way involves using the journal pages and cover provided at the end of this section. Choose the journal page which is appropriate for your students' developmental level. Duplicate the number of pages you need plus one copy of the cover for each student. Staple the pages into a booklet and allow your students to decorate them as they wish.

You can also have students create Science Journals by stapling loose-leaf paper between two sheets of construction paper.  A third method involves having them purchase a composition book for this purpose.

## Curriculum Links

Science knowledge is meaningless if it is not applied to life. The aim of science education is not to turn every student into a scientist, but to help students apply science knowledge and skills to everyday situations. The critical thinking and problem solving skills developed in science will enable students to become happier, more productive citizens.

Young children learn best when content areas are integrated rather than isolated. New information must be related to what they already know for it to be meaningful. As stated in *Early Childhood Education and the Elementary Principal,* "An integrated approach to curriculum recognizes that content areas in instruction are naturally interrelated, as they are in real life." (NAESP, 1990). They further recommend that content be integrated around themes.

To assist you in planning your instruction around themes, I have listed the possible themes for each lesson on its introductory page. Many of the lessons could be taught as a part of more than one thematic unit. For example, "Catch a Rainbow" would fit into a unit on color, light, rainbows, or weather. You'll need to examine your entire curriculum to determine where each lesson can be integrated.

Many areas of the curriculum are easy to connect with science. For instance, after the lesson "Seeds of all Sorts," students can measure seeds, act out the life cycle of a plant, make 15-bean soup, or do seed art. Math, music, art, writing, reading, and even creative movement can be integrated with most science lessons. To get you started with ideas, I have included suggestions for Curriculum Links in each lesson. Look for the Curriculum Link icon to locate these activities.

## Literature Connections

Using the thematic approach to instruction, elementary teachers have a unique opportunity to connect science with literature. Science concepts come alive for children through the pages of a book. For this reason, many of the *Wee Science* lessons introduce key concepts through children's literature. An open book icon will help you spot these activities. To help you locate these books in the library, I have included a bibliography of children's literature at the back of this book.

## Adaptations for Age

Even though Wee Science lessons were designed for the primary grades, they can easily be modified for use with upper elementary students. To adapt them for older children, pace the lessons more quickly and challenge older students to ecplore the concepts beyond the basics.

The lessons can also be adapted for very young children by incorporating developmentally appropriate practices. For example, many kindergarten teachers avoid having students do traditional worksheet activities in which children use crayons to circle responses. Instead, they allow their students to place moveable chips or markers on the answers they believe to be correct. This allows students to move their markers as they develop an understanding of the concept, enabling children to experience success rather than frustration. Kindergarten teachers can easily adapt the Wee Science worksheets to this format by having students place markers on their answers instrad of circling them with a crayon.

Advocates of developmentally appropriate practices also recommend that beginning writers avoid writing on lines until they develop necessary fine motor skills. With this in mind, I designed the worksheets with open spaces rather than lines for e responses. In situations where lines were needed, I included an alternative worksheet for beginning writers.

These are only a few of the possible ways to adapt lessons for particular age groups and developmental levels. In addition, many of the lessons include age-appropriate suggestions for young children and older students. The Adaptations for Age icon marks these lesson-specific suggestions.

## Science Materials

Teaching hands-on science is more difficult than teaching textbook science in one respect: locating the materials for students to put their "hands on." I won't belittle this problem by saying that most of the materials used are common household items. Even though most *are* everyday items, I recognize that you will invest time, effort, and money in gathering enough materials for each lesson. Plastic cups, bean seeds, and potting soil may not be expensive, but supplying your class with such materials on a regular basis can be quite costly.

Yet, hands-on materials are absolutely essential to cooperative process science. Problems in obtaining materials must be addressed and resolved if meaningful science instruction is to occur. Fortunately, using cooperative learning instead of individual instruction significantly reduces the amount of materials needed. Using a learning center approach further reduces the need for materials. However, at least a few sets of materials are needed for each lesson.

If your school's science budget is somewhat skimpy, creative planning can solve some of your problems in locating materials. One solution is to request that parents donate some of the more common household items. Write down the materials you need for the remainder of the year and send home this "wish list" with each student. In addition, ask your parent-teacher organization to help you purchase some non-consumable items like magnets, hand lenses, batteries, and wire. Local businesses, especially companies that rely heavily on science and technology, may support your efforts with a financial contribution.

If you are able to obtain some money but aren't sure where to order materials, consult the Science Resources at the back of this book. The companies listed specialize in supplying science books and materials to teachers. All of them have a toll-free number you can call for more information or to obtain a catalog.

## Safety Spotlight

When you incorporate hands-on experiences into your science lessons, be aware of safety considerations. Make sure you follow any safety guidelines issued by your district or state. Remember that students who have been given more freedom to explore don't instinctively know when exploration borders on being unsafe. They trust you to set the limits. Be especially cautious when working with flames, chemicals, glass, or electricity.

Many of the lessons in this book pose no possible danger to students at all. However, some of the lessons contain potential hazards if students are not properly supervised during the activities. In these lessons, I have identified and described the possible problems. Look for the Safety Spotlight icon next to activities which need careful supervision.

## Science Lesson Format

Since the lessons involve hands-on experiences and are somewhat lengthy, I attempted to make them as convenient as possible for you to teach. To make them more manageable, I wrote each one as a series of activities. Each activity is described on a separate activity card, and the cards are numbered in the suggested instructional sequence. You'll find the directions for each activity, along with the materials needed, on each activity card. Any advanced preparation needed for that activity is located on the page next to the card. All worksheets and patterns can be found at the end of the lesson. I also placed a compiled list of materials at the end of each lesson. Use this as a shopping list; check off each item as you gather materials in advance.

For your convenience, I included a brief summary of each lesson on its introductory page. Look for the pages with a test tube along the right edge; these pages mark the beginning of a complete lesson. In the upper right corner you'll find the lesson themes. Next to the test tube you'll find a list of activities your students will complete. Beside the test tube you'll also find a list of process skills and structures used in the lesson. When selecting a lesson, skim the introductory pages for pertinent information.

All of the lessons assume that students are seated in teams of four. Furthermore, each team should be divided into two sets of pairs for the partner activities. Assign teams and partners prior to the lesson to ensure that students are comfortable interacting with each other.

Use the icons to help you locate specific areas of interest. A complete index of icons is located at the beginning of this book.

## Ready . . . Set . . . Science!

With a knowledge of cooperative learning techniques and child-centered science instruction, you're ready to begin. Choose a lesson and discover the fun of *Wee Science!*

## Reference

**National Association of Elementary School Principals.** *Early Childhood Education and the Elementary School Principal.* NAESP, Alexandria, Virginia: 1990.

# Science Journal

**Name** _____

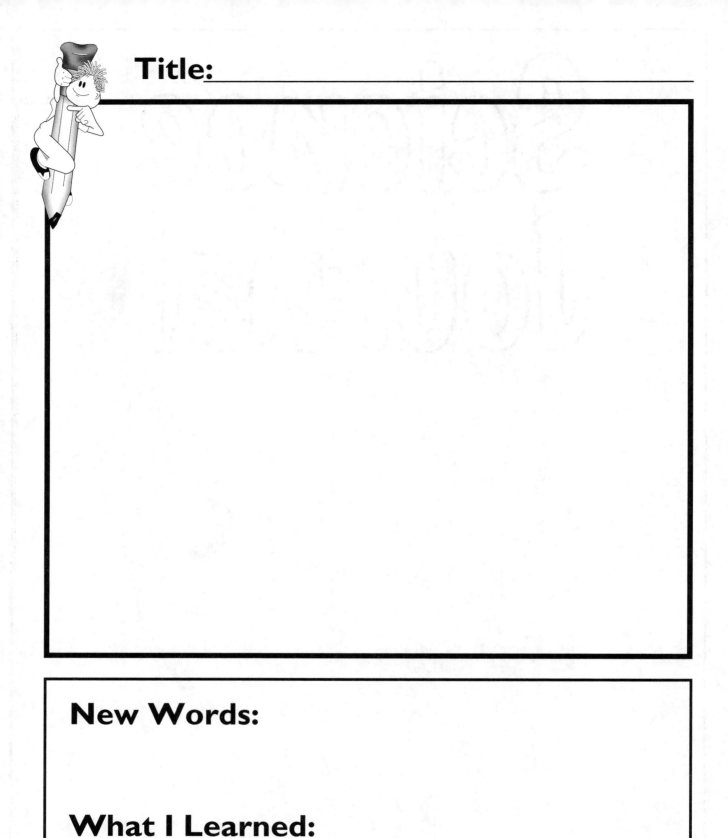

**Title:**

**New Words:**

**What I Learned:**

Laura Candler: *Wee Science*     ***Kagan Publishing*** • 1 (800) 933-2667 • www.KaganOnline.com

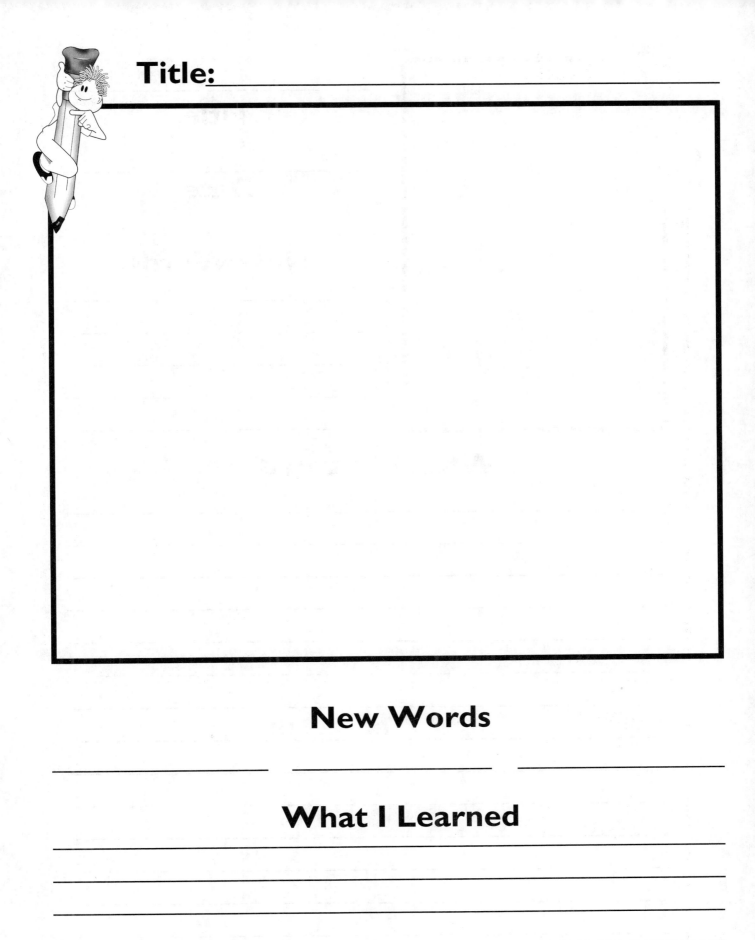

**Title:** _____

## New Words

_____  _____

## What I Learned

_____

_____

_____

_____

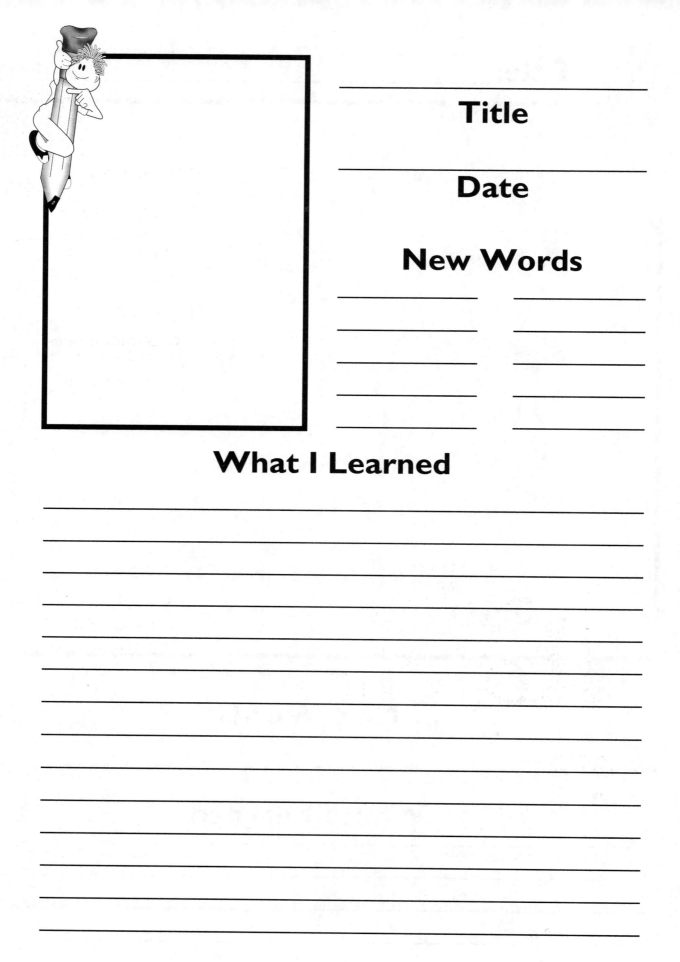

**Title**

**Date**

**New Words**

## What I Learned

Laura Candler: *Wee Science*    ***Kagan* Publishing** • 1 (800) 933-2667 • www.KaganOnline.com

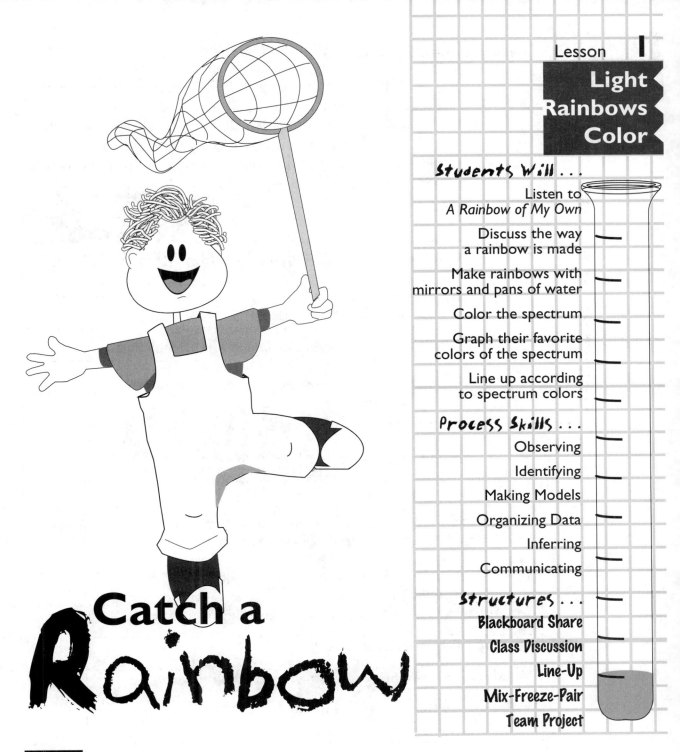

## Light Rainbows Color

### Students Will . . .

Listen to
*A Rainbow of My Own*

Discuss the way
a rainbow is made

Make rainbows with
mirrors and pans of water

Color the spectrum

Graph their favorite
colors of the spectrum

Line up according
to spectrum colors

### Process Skills . . .

Observing

Identifying

Making Models

Organizing Data

Inferring

Communicating

### Structures . . .

Blackboard Share

Class Discussion

Line-Up

Mix-Freeze-Pair

Team Project

# Catch a Rainbow

**C** hildren and adults alike are fascinated by rainbows. Studying rainbows provides a perfect opportunity to learn about light and color. In this lesson, your students will listen to *A Rainbow of My Own*. Then they'll use mirrors and pans of water to "catch" rainbows on white paper. They'll learn the colors of the spectrum and color rainbows accurately. They'll graph their favorite rainbow colors. Finally, they'll put on color tags and line up in spectrum order.

Some parts of this lesson can be completed in a learning center. Note the "Learning Center" icon next to these activities. If your students have not handled mirrors before, you may want to place a few mirrors in a learning center before you begin the lesson. Providing time for **Cooperative Play** in advance will keep your students from being distracted by their fascination with mirrors during the lesson.

## 1

### *Read a rainbow story using* TEACHER READS

**Materials for the Class:**
*A Rainbow of My Own* by Don Freeman

Read the story *A Rainbow of My Own* to your class. Tell your students that in a few minutes (or the next day) they'll catch a rainbow of their own.

## 2

### *Discuss rainbows using* MIX-FREEZE-PAIR

Tell students to "Mix" by walking quietly around the room. Then call out "Freeze!" When everyone is standing still, say "Pair!" Students should link arms with the person closest to them. Make sure everyone has a partner and call out one of the following questions for them to discuss. Repeat entire **Mix-Freeze-Pair-Discuss** sequence with remaining questions:

**Have you ever seen a rainbow?**

**What was the weather like when you saw the rainbow?**

**What do you think makes a rainbow?**

### *Practice Making Rainbow*

Before attempting this activity with students, try making a rainbow on your own. Making a rainbow can be tricky until you get the knack for it. Once you learn how, you'll be able to teach your children easily. You'll need a mirror, flat-bottomed pan with at least 2 inches of water, and a white piece of posterboard. Place the pan of water in the sun and hold the mirror under the surface of the water at a 45 degree angle. Move the white posterboard around in the path of the reflected light until a rainbow appears. If you have trouble, keep trying different positions until you see a vivid band of colors.

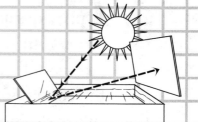

### Prepare Rainbow Role Cards

For the Rainbow Catching activity, duplicate one page of Rainbow Role Cards and cut them apart. Glue each card onto a quarter sheet (4 1/2" x 6") of construction paper. Use a different color for each role. Punch two holes along the top edge of each card and string yarn through so they can be worn around the neck.

Remind students to be careful when handling their mirrors during the "Making Rainbows" activity. If your mirrors are made of glass and the edges are sharp, tape the edges with masking tape to protect fingers.

## 3

### Demonstrate rainbows using TEACHER TALK

**Materials for the Demonstration:**
- 1 flashlight
- 1 set of four Rainbow Role Cards
- 1 small mirror
- 1 pan of water (at least 2 inches deep with a flat bottom)
- 1 small lump of modeling clay
- 1 piece of white posterboard (10" x 12")
- 1 box of crayons
- 4 index cards

The Rainbow Catching activity needs to be completed outdoors on a bright, sunny day. However, you may want to demonstrate the way to make a rainbow indoors so that students won't be distracted by their surroundings.

Tell your students that two things are needed to make a rainbow: sunlight and water drops. That's why rainbows can sometimes be seen when the sun shines after a rain. Sunlight looks white but is really made of many different colors together. When sunlight passes through water the light bends and separates into all the different colors.

Write the word **spectrum** on the board and tell your students that the word spectrum means all the colors of the rainbow. In the next activity they will make rainbows and try to see all the colors of the spectrum.

Before you distribute materials, use one team to help you demonstrate how to make a rainbow. Warn them that making a rainbow is tricky and especially difficult with just the light from the flashlight. Tell your students that it will be much easier outside in the sun, but you wanted to show them how to do it before going out. Follow these steps on the next page to demonstrate the procedure.

(continued on page 66)

**3 cont.**

### Demonstrate rainbows *(continued from page 65)*

1. Give each team member one of the four Rainbow Role Cards to wear. Assure them that everyone will have a chance to play each role, so it doesn't matter who puts on each role card first.

2. Hold the flashlight yourself and use it to represent the sun. Shine the flashlight onto the water at an angle.

3. Have the Rainbow Maker place the mirror into the pan of water at a 45 degree angle to catch the rays of light. Have them prop the mirror with the ball of clay.

4. Have the Rainbow Catcher hold the white poster board. The Rainbow Maker and the Rainbow Catcher will have to work together to make a rainbow appear on the poster board.

5. When the two students have made a rainbow, their teammates record the results by using the crayons to draw what they see on an index card.

6. Now have the Rainbow Maker and Rainbow Catcher switch role cards and take turns trying to make a rainbow appear. The others continue sketching the spectrum.

7. Finally, let the Recorders become the Rainbow Maker and Catcher. While they take turns making a rainbow, the other two record the results on their own index cards.

**4**

### Make rainbows using **TEAM PROJECT**

**Materials for each Team:**
1 set of four Rainbow Role Cards
1 small mirror
1 pan of water (at least 2 inches deep
   with a flat bottom)
1 small lump of modeling clay
1 piece of white posterboard (10"x12")
1 box of crayons
4 index cards

After demonstrating the procedure indoors, take the class outside on a bright, sunny day. Give each team a set of role cards and have each person wear one. Remind them that they will be trading roles later. Distribute the pans of water, mirrors, clay, crayons, and index cards.

Instruct the teams to try making their own rainbows. Monitor their efforts carefully because catching a rainbow takes coordination and some students may have difficulty with this task. Remind the Recorders to draw what they see on their index cards.

***Make Demonstration Rainbow***
Cut out the arc pattern and follow the directions given on the Demonstration Rainbow page.

**5**

### *Discuss the spectrum using* CLASS DISCUSSION

**Materials for the Class:**
1 Demonstration Rainbow

**Materials for each Team:**
Index cards used in previous activity

When you return to the room, ask students to volunteer the colors that they saw in their rainbows. Remind them to refer to their index cards for this information. List the colors on the board as the students name them. After you list each color, put the colored arc from the demonstration rainbow next to the word. The arcs will not be in the correct order at this point.

Tell your students that it's difficult to see each individual color, but scientists know that all rainbows have the same seven colors in the same order. From bottom to top, the colors are red, orange, yellow, green, blue, indigo, and violet. Tell your students that **indigo** is a dark blue-purple color. Violet is just another name for purple. Make sure all these colors on the board.

Tell your students that some people remember the colors of the rainbow by making a name out of the first letter of each color. Written together, those initials spell "Roy G. Biv." As you review the correct order of the colors, rearrange the colored arcs of the Demonstration Rainbow so that they form an accurate spectrum. Write the word spectrum on the board again and remind them that this word means all the colors of the rainbow.

**6**

## Color rainbows using INDIVIDUALS DRAW

**Materials for each Student:**
1 copy of the Color a Rainbow worksheet

**Materials for each Team:**
1 box of crayons

Give each student one copy of the Color a Rainbow worksheet. Have them use the key to color the rainbow correctly. If they don't have an indigo crayon, they can blend blue and purple together.

### Prepare Graph Materials

Draw a blank bar graph on the board or chart paper. The grid should be 7 blocks wide and about 10 blocks tall. Make each block approximately 3 inches square. Then cut ten 2-inch square pieces of each of the 7 spectrum colors. Write the names of one color under each column on the class graph. (See illustration.)

**7**

## Graph favorite colors using BLACKBOARD SHARE

**Materials for the Class:**
1 blank class graph
box of colored paper squares (2")
masking tape

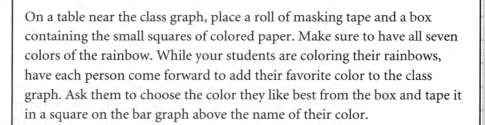

On a table near the class graph, place a roll of masking tape and a box containing the small squares of colored paper. Make sure to have all seven colors of the rainbow. While your students are coloring their rainbows, have each person come forward to add their favorite color to the class graph. Ask them to choose the color they like best from the box and tape it in a square on the bar graph above the name of their color.

After everyone has added their favorite color to the chart, discuss the results with them. Ask questions like "Which color is the most popular?" and "How many more people like red than blue?" Let them make up their own questions, too.

# Class Color Graph

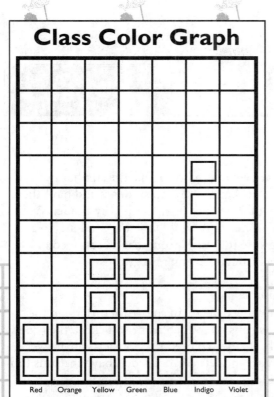

Red  Orange  Yellow  Green  Blue  Indigo  Violet

### Make Color Signs

Use a full 9" x 12" sheet of colored construction paper for each sign. Divide the total number of students by 7 and make that number of signs in each of the following colors: red, orange, yellow, green, blue, indigo, and violet. Write the name of the color on each sign in bold letters. For the extra students, cut out large yellow "sun" signs. Draw a smiling face on one side and a frowning face on the other side of the suns. Punch holes through each sign and string yarn through the holes so that they can be easily worn.

BLUE

## 8

## Sequence colors using **LINE-UP**

**Materials for each Student:**
1 color or sun sign

### Step One: Explaining the problem

To prepare your children for the Rainbow **Line-Up,** read the following story:

*Once long ago the sun was shining brightly upon the Earth, just as it does now. It warmed the soil and made the flowers bloom. Sometimes the clouds came and rain fell, but the sun didn't mind. When the clouds broke apart after the storm, the sun would show off by making a beautiful rainbow.*

*One day a huge, dark cloud covered the sun and rain began to fall. Rain fell all the first day and all the second day. The sun waited for the rain to stop, but the rain kept falling. The storm lasted for five days and nights.*

*Finally, the clouds cleared away and the rain stopped. The sun was so happy that it made a tremendous rainbow across the sky. But when the sun looked at the rainbow it became very sad again. For the colors of the rainbow were all mixed up!*

*(continued on page 8)*

**8 cont.**

*Sequence colors* *(continued from page 7)*

### Step Two: Forming teams

Now ask your class if they are willing to help make the sun happy again. First, give the yellow sun signs to several students and have them come to the front of the room. Turn the signs to the frown side. Next, randomly give out the rest of the color signs. Tell your students to get in groups of seven, making sure that each group has all seven colors. Young children may need assistance getting into groups.

### Step Three: Sequencing colors

Now have your students line up correctly in spectrum order. Let the students who are playing the suns go to each team and check the order. Let the suns use the worksheets they colored previously as an answer key. When all the rainbows are in their correct order, have the suns flip their signs to the smiling side.

### Step Four: Repeating activity

If time allows, repeat the activity by using **Mix-Freeze-Pair.** Call out "Mix!" and have the students move about the room. When you say "Freeze!" they stand still. Call out "Pair!" and have them quickly find a partner. Finally, say "Trade!" and have them trade color or sun signs.

Now have the students form groups of seven and sequence themselves properly. As before, the suns check the line ups.

### Step Five: Discussing spectrums

When the activity is over, ask your students if they think the colors of the rainbow could really get mixed up as they did in the story. Make sure they understand that the colors of the spectrum always appear in the same order and that the story was just for fun.

### Science Journal Suggestions

**Vocabulary:** rainbow, spectrum, indigo, violet
**Illustrations:** rainbows, sketch of experiment set-up, class graph
**Writing:**    describe experiment, list colors of spectrum, answer questions about class graph, make up questions about class graph, explain how a rainbow is made, write a story about seeing a rainbow

# Materials Check List

**For Teacher:**
- ❑ *A Rainbow of My Own* by Don Freeman
- ❑ 1 Demonstration Rainbow
- ❑ 1 blank class graph
- ❑ 1 box of colored paper squares (2")
- ❑ 1 masking tape
- ❑ 1 flashlight

**For each Team:**
- ❑ 1 set of four Rainbow Role Cards
- ❑ 1 small mirror
- ❑ 1 pan of water (at least 2 inches deep with a flat bottom)
- ❑ 1 small lump of modeling clay
- ❑ 1 piece of white posterboard (10" x 12")
- ❑ 1 box of crayons
- ❑ 4 index cards

**For each Student:**
- ❑ 1 copy of the Color A Rainbow worksheet
- ❑ 1 color or sun sign (see Step 8)

## Curriculum Links

### 1. Art - Mixing colors
Teach students about primary and secondary colors. Let students try mixing the three primary colors to get the secondary colors. To do this, give them small cups of colored water, eye droppers or straws, and waxed paper. Have them drop colored water onto the waxed paper and mix to blend colors.

### 2. Creative Movement - Rainbow dancing
Give students crepe paper streamers in rainbow colors. Play soft music and have them arch the streamers over their heads as they move to the music.

### 3. Literature - Reading color poems
Read color poems such as those found in *Hailstones and Halibut Bones* by Mary O'Neill.

### 4. Science - Making color viewers
Help each student cut a 4" x 8" rectangular opening in a paper grocery bag about 3" from the bottom. Give each team four different colors of cellophane. Assign each person on the team a different color. Have them cut a 6" x 10" rectangle of cellophane and tape it over the bag opening to make a pull-on color viewer (see illustration). Have them pull the bags over their heads and adjust to fit by rolling up the bottom edge of the paper bag.

Let them wear their color viewers around to see how the world looks in a different color. Then have each person draw a picture using only the four colors used in the team's color viewers. Let the students trade pictures and color viewers so they can see how each illustration looks different when viewed through a different color.

### 5. Language Arts - Writing color poems
Have students write poems about the colors of the spectrum. Acrostics are easy color poems to create. Write the letters of the color down the left side of a sheet of paper. Then write a word or phrase for each letter which describes an object or a feeling associated with that color. (see example)

**G**rapes
**R**ipe Granny-Smith apples
**E**xciting
**E**vergreen trees
**N**ew grass in the spring

# Demonstration Rainbow

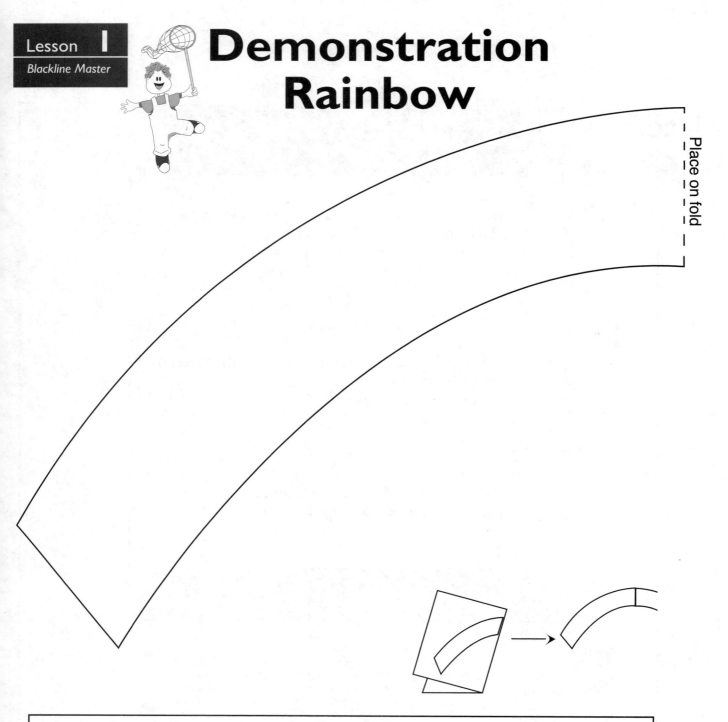

Place on fold

## Directions

1. Cut out the rainbow arc pattern.

2. Make 1 arc in each of these colors: red, orange, yellow, green, blue, indigo, violet.

3. To make each arc, fold a 12" x 18" sheet of construction paper in half. Place the pattern with dotted edge on the fold and trace.

4. Cut around tracing and open arc.

5. Assemble rainbow during lesson by stacking colors in spectrum order.

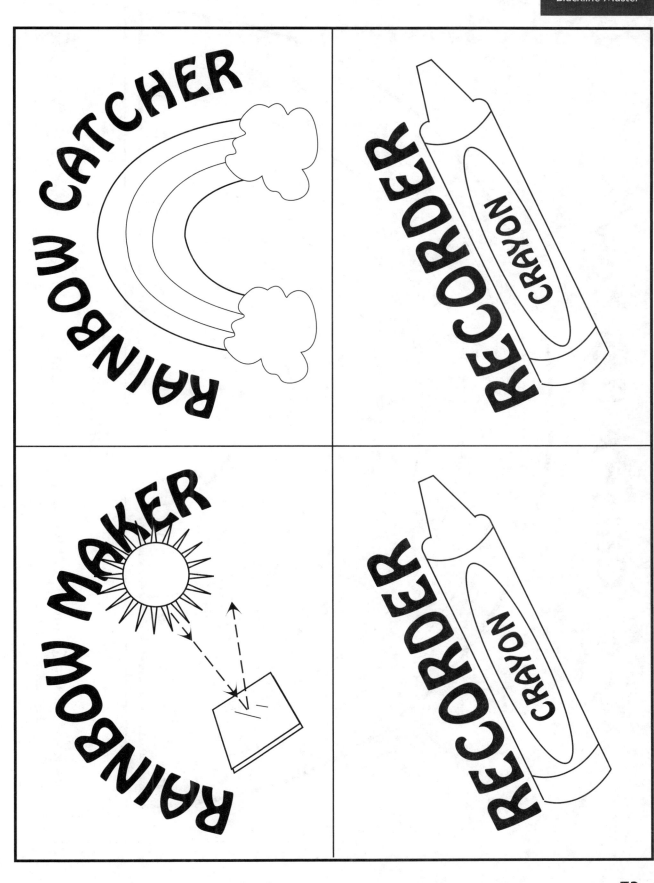

RAINBOW CATCHER

RECORDER

CRAYON

RAINBOW MAKER

RECORDER

CRAYON

# Color A Rainbow

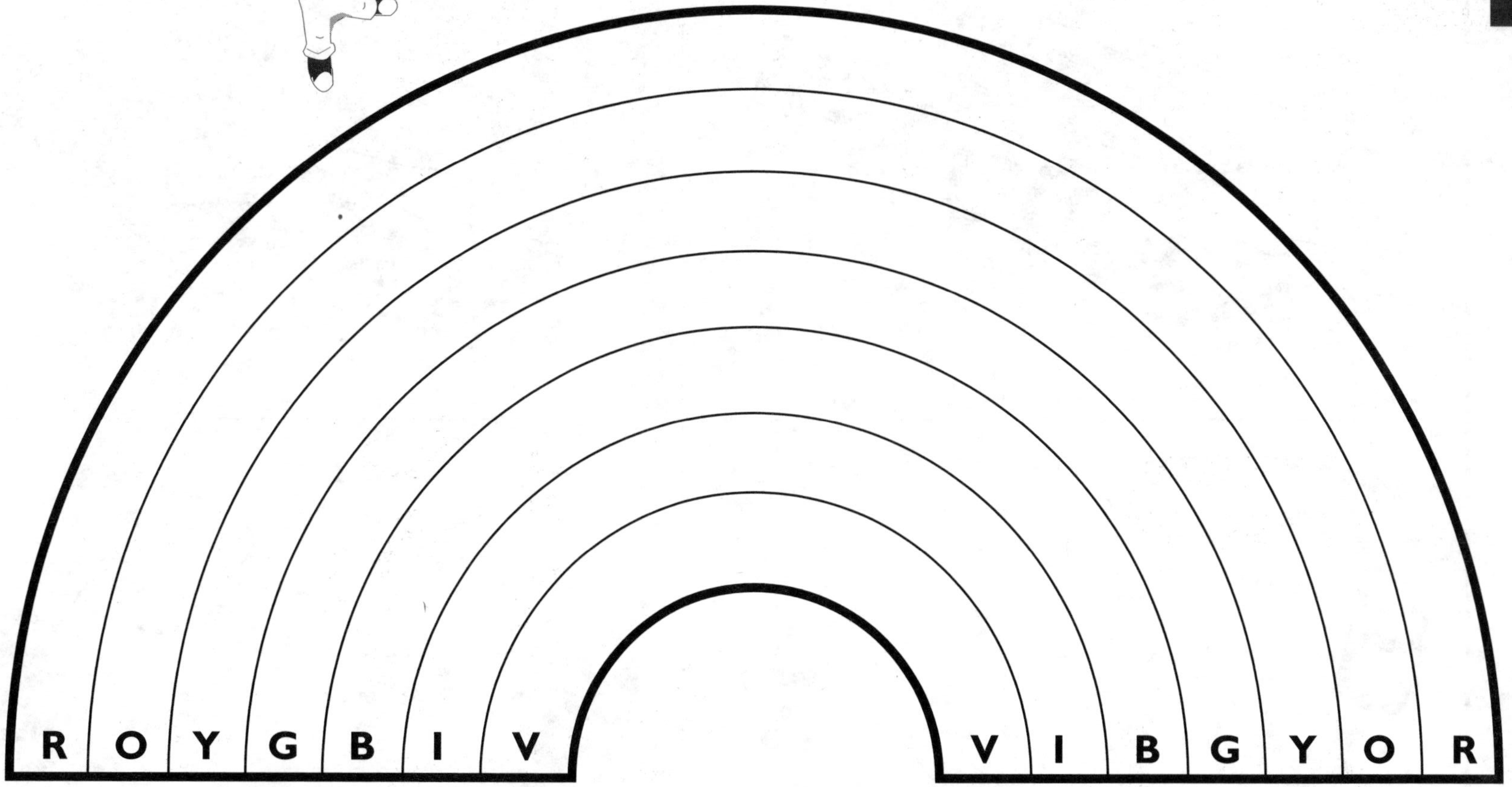

**Color Key**

R=Red    O=Orange    Y=Yellow    G=Green    B=Blue    I=Indigo    V=Violet

ROYGBIV

VIBGYOR

# Magnet Magic

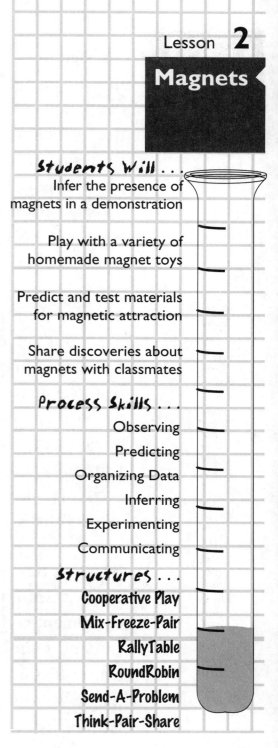

**M**agnets are magic to young children. A magnet's ability to attract and repel with an invisible force field provides endless opportunities for exploration. This lesson allows children to discover basic properties of magnets and encourages them to share their findings with others.

To begin the lesson, you will show your students two homemade magnet toys without telling them that the objects contain magnets. Your children will try to figure out what makes them work. Using **Send-A-Problem,** you'll provide time for teams to play with homemade magnetic toys and make discoveries on their own. They'll share their discoveries in a **Class RoundRobin.** Later they'll make and test predictions about what materials are attracted to a magnet. Finally, they'll play a game to practice what they learned.

Many of the activities in this lesson can be adapted for use in a learning center. Since every child needs a chance to explore a variety of magnets and materials, some of the activities may be too expensive to prepare for whole class use. To minimize expenses, prepare one set of materials and place them in a science center. After explaining each activity, send each team in turn to the learning center to complete the activity. A circular "Learning Center" symbol appears next to each activity that can be adapted for use in a science center.

Be aware that magnets may be destructive to certain items in your classroom. Magnetic fields can damage some electrical equipment and information storing devices. Don't allow students to hold magnets near the items listed in the warning below. If you allow students to move around freely with magnets, post large red stop signs on objects that can be harmed by magnets.

*Warning!*
Magnets are potentially dangerous to these items:

| | | |
|---|---|---|
| computers | telephones | loudspeakers |
| diskettes | credit cards | watches |
| audio tapes | microwave ovens | VCRs |
| video tapes | televisions | answering machines |

You'll need to make a set of simple magnetic toys for this lesson. You can find directions for making these toys on pages 84 and 85. I have found that one of the best places to buy inexpensive magnets is an electronics store such as Radio Shack.

Make at least one Floating Paper Clip toy and one Bouncing Ring toy for the **Think-Pair-Share** activity. For the **Send-A-Problem,** make as many toys as needed (at least one per team). If possible, make two of each toy to allow more students to actually get their "hands-on" one. The toys will be passed from one team to another during a **Send-A-Problem** activity, so make sure that each toy is placed in a large baggie or shoe box to avoid losing parts. To prepare the toys, follow the instructions found on the page entitled "Directions for Magnetic Toys."

## *Inferring the presence of magnets* using **THINK-PAIR-SHARE**

**Materials for the Class:**
1 Floating Paper Clip toy
1 Bouncing Rings toy

Make sure each person in the class is sitting next to a partner for this activity.

Hold up the Floating Paper Clip toy. Take the paper clip out of the magnetic field so that it drops down and hangs from the thread. Then hold it back up to the magnet so that it "floats" again. Ask your students, "What could make the magnet float in the air like this?" Have them think of their own answer for a few seconds. On a signal from you, have them pair with their partner to discuss their ideas. Then have them share their guesses with the class. Show them the secret magnet that makes the toy work, but don't tell them too much about it. Assure them that they will have a chance to play with the toy soon.

Now hold up the Bouncing Rings toy. Ask "Why are these rings floating apart from each other?" Have them think, pair, and share their ideas as before. Refrain from explaining that the magnetic rings are repelling each other; just say that they will soon have a chance to play with the rings themselves.

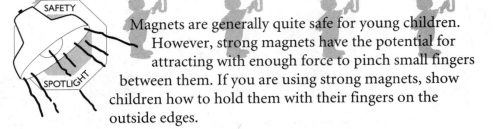

SAFETY

SPOTLIGHT

Magnets are generally quite safe for young children. However, strong magnets have the potential for attracting with enough force to pinch small fingers between them. If you are using strong magnets, show children how to hold them with their fingers on the outside edges.

Another safety consideration involves the Oily Iron Bits toy. Warn children about handling the glass jar of oil carefully to prevent breakage.

## 2

### *Playing with magnetic toys* using SEND-A-PROBLEM

**Materials for the Class:**
2 of each type of toy as described in the Directions for Magnetic Toys on pages 84–85

### *Step One:  Exploring the first toy*
Make sure your students are in teams of four. They may be seated at tables or grouped by teams on the floor. Give each team one type of magnetic toy. Since you should have two sets of each, give one toy to each pair of students. For example, give two sets of Bouncing Rings to the first team, two sets of Magnetic Windows to the second team, and so on.

Tell your students that they will have five minutes to play with their toys before passing them to another team. Ask them "What can you discover about your toy?" Encourage pairs of students to play together and talk about their discoveries. Monitor this part of the activity carefully to make sure everyone is sharing and working together.

### *Step Two:  Passing toys*
When the five minutes are up, designate one person on each team to be the Toy Passer. He or she collects the toys from team members and makes sure each toy is back in its bag or box. The Toy Passer then takes the toys to the next team. Pass the toys in an organized manner so that all teams will eventually be able to play with all toys.

### *Step Three:  Exploring magnetic toys*
For each round of the activity, give five minutes for team members to explore their magnetic toys. Continue passing and playing until each team has had a chance to use each toy. Let a different child be the Toy Passer for each round.

## 3

### *Sharing discoveries using* CLASS ROUNDROBIN

Have everyone sit in a large circle with all the magnetic toys in the center. Ask each person to tell something they discovered while playing with one of the toys. Start by sharing one discovery yourself. For instance, "I noticed that when I tried to push the rings together they jumped apart." Have the person on your right say the next discovery and so on around the circle. If someone doesn't want to share an idea, they may pass. However, ask them again at the end of the **RoundRobin** if they want to share something they found out. If students want to hold a toy while they talk about it, let them take the toy from the center of the circle.

Use this time to talk with your students about the concepts you want them to learn. Teach them the special words (like attract and repel) used when discussing magnets. You may want to discuss some of the following ideas. Use whatever terms and concepts are appropriate for the developmental level of your students. Don't give too much information about the types of objects magnets attract because this will spoil their prediction activity.

### 3 cont.

### *Magnet Concepts*

- Every magnet has an invisible magnetic field around it.
- Iron bits or iron filings will line up to show a magnet's force field.
- A magnet's force is stronger at the ends, which are called poles.
- Magnets have two poles, called a north and a south pole.
- Between two magnets, like poles repel and unlike poles attract. In other words, two north poles will push against each other but a north pole and a south pole will pull together.
- A compass contains a magnet and can be moved by a magnet.
- Magnets attract some objects and not others.
- All materials attracted by a magnet are made of metal, but not all metals are attracted by a magnet. (Most magnetic objects students will handle contain iron or steel.)
- Magnets can attract through most materials.

**Prepare Magnet Test Kits:**
Prepare two Kits for each learning center or team. To make each kit, place the following items in a baggie: paper clip, marble, aluminum foil scrap, iron nail, crayon, penny, rubber band, scissors, and a safety pin.

## 4

### Testing for magnetic attraction using RALLYTABLE

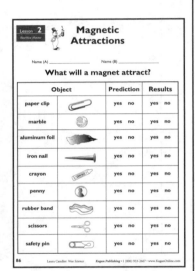

Lesson 2

**Magnetic Attractions**

Name (A) _____ Name (B) _____

**What will a magnet attract?**

| Object | | Prediction | Results |
|---|---|---|---|
| paper clip | | yes  no | yes  no |
| marble | | yes  no | yes  no |
| aluminum foil | | yes  no | yes  no |
| iron nail | | yes  no | yes  no |
| crayon | | yes  no | yes  no |
| penny | | yes  no | yes  no |
| rubber band | | yes  no | yes  no |
| scissors | | yes  no | yes  no |
| safety pin | | yes  no | yes  no |

86        Laura Candler: Wee Science        *Kagan Publishing* • 1 (800) 933-2667 • www.KaganOnline.com

**Materials for each Pair:**
1 Magnet Test Kit
1 magnet
1 Magnetic Attractions worksheet
2 different color crayons

### Step One:  Introducing the activity
Give each pair of students one Magnet Test Kit, one worksheet, and two crayons. Do not give them a magnet yet! Tell them that they are going to predict which materials in the bag will be attracted to the magnet. Tell them that a prediction is what they think is going to happen. The result is what actually does happen.

Have each person choose one color crayon and write their name on one line of the worksheet in that color. Throughout the activity they should use the same color crayon.

### Step Two:  Making predictions
Now have students take turns making predictions about which materials will be attracted to a magnet. Both students make predictions about every item, using their own color crayon. Have Person A name the first item (paper clip) and both students circle either "YES" or "NO" under the "Prediction" heading. Next, Person B names the second item (marble) and both circle their prediction. They continue until all predictions are made.

*(continued on page 81)*

**4 cont.**

### Testing for magnetic attraction (continued from page 80)

#### Step Three: Testing predictions
After each pair has made their predictions, give them a magnet. Have them take turns touching a magnet to the materials to test their guesses. Instruct them to both circle the correct answer under the word "Result."

#### Step Four: Discussing results
When everyone has finished, be sure to discuss the results. Some students may be upset that their predictions were "wrong." Reassure them that scientists make guesses about what will happen in experiments, but they don't say they are "wrong" if the experiment doesn't work the way they thought it would.

Duplicate and cut apart enough Object Signs so that half of your class can wear one sign each. Mount each sign on a half sheet of red construction paper. Then duplicate and cut apart enough Magnet Signs so that the rest of the class can wear one sign each. Mount each Magnet sign on a half sheet of blue construction paper. Punch two holes in both sets of signs and string yarn through them so that they can be worn around students' necks.

**5**

### Reviewing concepts using MIX-FREEZE-PAIR

**Materials for the Class:**
an equal number of Magnet and Object Signs (enough for each person to have one)

#### Step One: Distributing signs
Tell your students that they are going to play a game to practice what they have learned. Each person will play the part of a magnet or an object. Make sure you have an equal number of Magnet Signs and Object Signs. Randomly pass out the signs and have students hang them around their necks.

#### Step Two: Practicing concepts
Say "Mix!" and have everyone walk quietly around the room. Then call out "Freeze!" When everyone is still, say "Pair!" Each "Magnet" must find an "Object" to pair with. Since the Magnet and Object cards are mounted on different colors of construction paper, point out that red signs should pair with blue signs. With an uneven number of students, two magnets can pair with one object.

*(continued on page 82)*

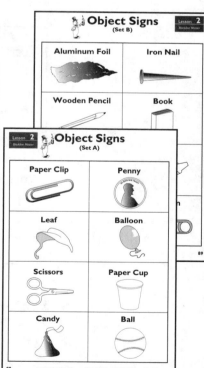

## 5 cont.

### Reviewing concepts (continued from page 81)

After the students pair, have them face each other holding their hands up with their palms out. If the "Object" is magnetic, the two touch palms. If the "Object" is nonmagnetic, the two leave a space between their palms (see illustration).

Do a silent "quick check" to make sure that the only students with hands touching are those whose object is a safety pin, iron nail, scissors, or paper clip. All other objects are nonmagnetic.

### Step Three: Exchanging signs

While students are still in pairs, have each person take off their sign and hang it around their partner's neck. Everyone assumes a new identity for the next round of **Mix-Freeze-Pair.** Continue playing the game as time allows.

## 6

### Exploring magnets using COOPERATIVE PLAY

Place all the magnets and materials in a learning center or on a table. Let each team or pair of students have a chance to visit the center and play with the materials one more time. This gives them a chance to explore the new concepts they learned in this lesson.

### Science Journal Suggestions
**Vocabulary:** magnet, attract, repel, north pole, south pole
**Illustrations:** pictures of different types of magnets, pictures of magnetic toys
**Writing:** sentences about what was learned, description of favorite magnetic toy

# Materials Check List

### For the Class:
- ❏ Floating Paper Clip toy
- ❏ Bouncing Rings toy
- ❏ 2 of each type of toy described in the Directions for Magnetic Toys
- ❏ an equal number of Magnet and Object signs (enough for each person to have one)

### For each Pair:
- ❏ 1 Magnet Test Kit
- ❏ 1 magnet
- ❏ 1 Magnetic Attractions worksheet
- ❏ 2 different color crayons

## Curriculum Links

### 1. Art - Painting with magnets

Cut sheets of art paper to fit inside a small cake pan or flat-bottomed container. Drop blobs of paint on the paper and place several magnetic objects on the paper. Steel ball bearings or metal washers work well. Let students work in pairs. One student holds the pan while the other moves a strong magnet underneath. Have them drag the magnetic objects through the paint and across the paper to make patterns or pictures.

### 2. Math - Measuring magnet strength

Give each team a variety of magnets along with a paper clip and a ruler. Have them take turns placing a magnet at the end of the ruler and slowly sliding the paper clip down the ruler. Another student can record the distance at which the paper clip is attracted to the magnet.

### 3. Science - Magnetizing an object

Give each student a strong magnet and a magnetic object such as a pair of scissors or an iron nail. Show them how to magnetize the object by stroking it repeatedly in one direction with the magnet. Let them test the strength of their new magnet about every 20 strokes by dipping it into a pile of paper clips or staples.

# Directions for Magnetic Toys

## Magnetic Window

### Materials
clear vinyl envelope or jacket, iron filings, clear packaging tape, two magnets

### Instructions
Purchase a clear vinyl jacket (the type used to protect important documents) from an office supply store. Pour about ½ teaspoon iron filing inside. Tape the top edge closed. Place two magnets with the "window."

## Amazing Maze

### Materials
Amazing Maze worksheet, small paper clip, thin sheet of cardboard or poster board (8" x 10"), one magnet, gallon-sized ziptop bag

### Instructions
Cut out the mouse on the Amazing Maze worksheet. Tape a small paper clip to the back of the mouse. Glue the maze onto the cardboard or poster board. Place the magnet, mouse, and maze in a large ziptop bag.

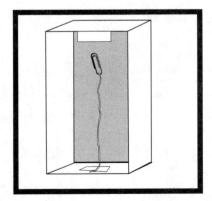

## Floating Paper Clip

### Materials
shoe box, magnet, thread, paper clip, construction paper, tape

### Instructions
Stand the box on one end and tape the magnet in the top. Hide the magnet by covering it with a small piece of construction paper. Tie the thread to the paper clip. Tape the thread to the bottom of the box so that the paper clip floats near the magnet without touching it. Trim away the extra thread.

# Directions for Magnetic Toys

## Bouncing Rings

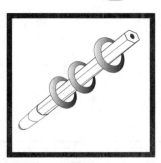

### Materials
unsharpened pencil, three ceramic ring magnets, gallon-sized ziptop bag

### Instructions
Place the pencil and ring magnets into the bag.

## Fishing With Magnets

### Materials
magnet, shoebox, unsharpened pencil, thread, magnetic and nonmagnetic objects

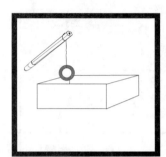

### Instructions
Tie the magnet to the thread and the thread to the pencil. Place a variety of magnetic and nonmagnetic objects in the box for students to fish for. Try to use objects that are *not* on the Magnetic Attractions worksheet.

## Oily Iron Bits

### Materials
small jar with tight-fitting lid, iron filings, two strong magnets, cooking or baby oil, tape or hot glue gun

### Instructions
Pour about a teaspoon iron filings into the jar. Completely fill the jar with oil and secure the lid tightly. Use tape or a hot glue gun to seal the lid.

## Compass Turner

### Materials
compass, two magnets, ziptop bag

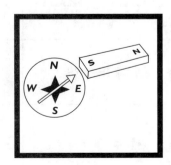

### Instructions
Place the magnets and compass in the bag.

# Magnetic Attractions

Name (A) _____     Name (B) _____

# What will a magnet attract?

| Object | | Prediction | Results |
|--------|---|-----------|---------|
| paper clip |  | yes    no | yes    no |
| marble | | yes    no | yes    no |
| aluminum foil | | yes    no | yes    no |
| iron nail | | yes    no | yes    no |
| crayon | | yes    no | yes    no |
| penny | | yes    no | yes    no |
| rubber band | | yes    no | yes    no |
| scissors | | yes    no | yes    no |
| safety pin | | yes    no | yes    no |

# Magnet
# Signs

| **Magnet** | **Magnet** |
|---|---|
| N S | N S |
| **Magnet** | **Magnet** |
| N S | N S |
| **Magnet** | **Magnet** |
| | |
| **Magnet** | **Magnet** |
| N S | N S |

# ¡Object Signs
## (Set A)

| | |
|---|---|
| **Paper Clip**  | **Penny**  |
| **Leaf** 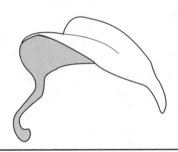 | **Balloon**  |
| **Scissors**  | **Paper Cup**  |
| **Candy**  | **Ball**  |

| | |
|---|---|
| **Aluminum Foil** | **Iron Nail** |
| **Wooden Pencil** | **Book** |
| **Marble** | **Crayon** CRAYOLA |
| **Rubber Band** | **Safety Pin** |

# Amazing Maze

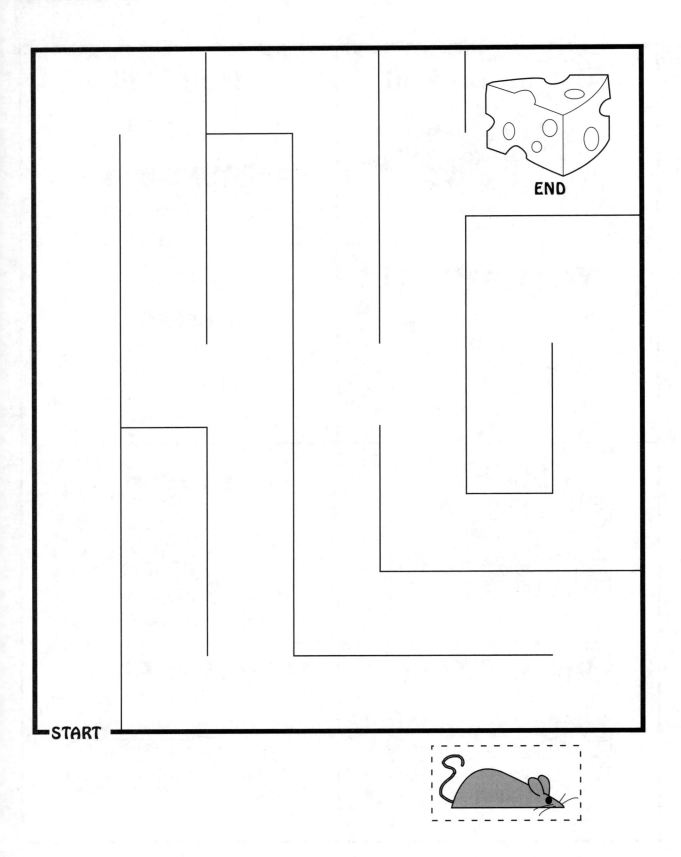

END

START

Laura Candler: *Wee Science*    ***Kagan* Publishing** • 1 (800) 933-2667 • www.KaganOnline.com

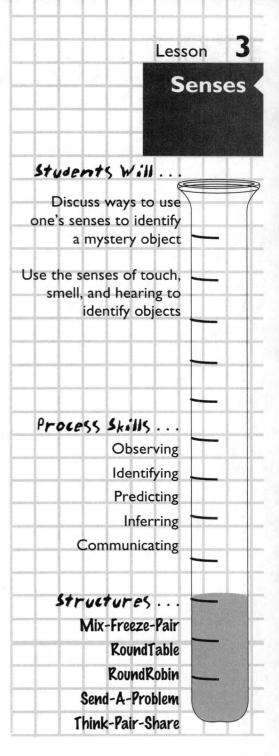

## Students Will . . .

Discuss ways to use
one's senses to identify
a mystery object

Use the senses of touch,
smell, and hearing to
identify objects

## Process Skills . . .

Observing

Identifying

Predicting

Inferring

Communicating

## Structures . . .

Mix-Freeze-Pair

RoundTable

RoundRobin

Send-A-Problem

Think-Pair-Share

# What's the Sense?

hat child hasn't shaken a wrapped present in order to guess its contents? This lesson incorporates the fun of solving such mysteries with the study of the human senses. These activities focus on developing the senses of smell, touch, and hearing. Your students will use their senses to predict the contents of several wrapped presents. Then they will use their senses to infer the contents of several Mystery Bags.

The Mystery Bag activity can be completed in a learning center. If you use the learning center approach, introduce the lesson to the entire class first. Then place four Mystery Bags and a set of worksheets at a workstation. Note the Learning Center icon next to each activity that can be completed in this manner.

### *Wrap presents*

Wrap two "presents" with colorful giftwrap. The first present should be a hardcover book, wrapped directly (without placing the book in a box). The second present should be a box containing wooden or plastic blocks.

**1**

## *Discussing presents using* THINK-PAIR-SHARE

**Materials for the Class:**
1 wrapped book
1 wrapped box containing wooden or plastic blocks

Have students sit in a circle with each person sitting next to a partner. Ask your students if they have ever tried to figure out what was inside a present before opening it.

### *Step One: Discussing ideas*

Ask them to think of ways they could figure out what's inside a wrapped present. Ask them to pair with a partner to discuss their ideas. Call on several students to share ideas with the class. Write some of their ideas on the board or on chart paper. Point out that they would use some of their senses to figure out what's inside. Review the five senses.

### *Step Two: Making guesses*

Show your students the gift-wrapped book and ask them how they could figure out what it is. If someone suggests seeing how heavy it is, let them hold the book. If they suggest shaking it, let them shake it. Discuss the senses that are being used. For instance, if a child wants to shake it to hear if it rattles, tell the class that they are using their sense of hearing. Finally, ask students to think about what's inside then pair with their partner to discuss their guesses. Call on students to share their ideas with the class. Write down some guesses, and then choose a child to open the present.

### *Step Three: Repeating activity*

Next, show your students the wrapped box containing blocks. Let a few students hold the box and make statements about the contents. Again, discuss the senses being used. Then have them **Think-Pair-Share** their guesses. Write down a few guesses and let someone open the box.

### Prepare demonstration bag

Place a small object inside a plain paper bag. The object should be able to be identified by touch, smell, hearing, or all three. Possible items include: a handful of rice or cereal, several marbles, coffee beans, a candy cane, a feather, an orange, a wind-up watch, a seashell, or crayons. Scrunch the top of the bag together and place a rubberband around it. A student should be able slip a hand inside without being able to see the contents.

## 2

### Introducing the Mystery Bags using TEACHER TALK

**Materials for the Class:**
1 demonstration Mystery Bag

**Materials for each Team:**
1 or more Mystery Bags
crayons or colored pencils
scissors

**Materials for each Student:**
2 "What's in the Bag?" worksheets

Hold up the demonstration Mystery Bag you prepared earlier. Tell them that it's a "Mystery Bag" and ask them if they know what a "mystery" is. Explain that a mystery is something that you don't know but might be able to figure out.

Tell your students that they are going to use some of their senses to figure out what's inside each bag. They will be allowed to reach inside and touch the object, but they may not look inside the bag before making their guess.

Explain that they are going to pass the bag around the team. Each person is going to say a sentence about the object without making a guess about what is in the bag. Model this for them by reaching into the demonstration bag and making several statements such as the ones below.

> *It's cold.*
> *It feels soft and furry.*
> *It sounds like sand when I shake it.*
> *It smells strong.*
> *It feels scratchy.*
> *It's heavy.*

## **3**

### *Guessing the object using* **THINK-PAIR-SHARE**

Now have them think about what might be in the Mystery Bag. Let them pair with their partner to discuss their ideas. Call on a few students to share their guesses with the class. Finally, open the bag and show them the contents.

### *Prepare team bags*

Prepare one Mystery Bag for each team. Write a number on the outside of each bag to keep them separate.

## **4**

### *Passing Mystery Bags using* **ROUNDTABLE**

**Materials for each Team:**
1 or more Mystery Bags
crayons or colored pencils
scissors

Give each team one Mystery Bag. Have the person you give it to reach inside and touch the object without looking. Ask them to tell their team something about what's in the bag but remind them not to make a guess about the object.

After the first person tells a sentence about what's in the bag, have them pass it to the person beside them. The next person reaches inside and says something about the object. Have them continue passing the bag until everyone thinks they know what's inside.

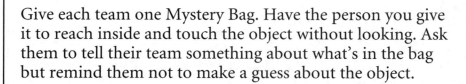

**5**

## *Drawing guesses using* **INDIVIDUALS DRAW**

**Materials for each Student:**
2 "What's in the Bag?" worksheets

When all teams are ready, give each person two copies of the "What's in the Bag?" worksheet. Have them cut the worksheets in half so they have four separate bag pictures. Have them write the bag number in the space at the top of the first picture. Then ask them to draw the object they think is in the bag. Then tell them to circle the name of the sense that was most helpful in figuring out the contents of the Mystery Bag.

**6**

## *Sharing guesses using* **ROUNDROBIN**

In **RoundRobin** fashion, have each person hold up their drawing and tell their teammates about it. They should also name the sense that helped them the most.

**7**

## *Checking guesses using* **ROUNDTABLE**

Have team members pass the bag one more time. This time they may peek into the bag to see if their guess was correct. Tell them not to let the other teams find out what's inside. Remind them to keep the what's inside the bags a "mystery."

### 8

*Sending Mystery Bags using* **SEND-A-PROBLEM**

When all teams are ready, have one teammate deliver their team's Mystery Bag to the next team. Establish a pattern for passing the bags so that teams will be sure to get a different bag each time. Have your students repeat the **RoundTable-Drawing-RoundRobin** sequence described above with each bag. Continue until all teams have guessed the contents of four different Mystery Bags.

### 9

*Discussing the senses using* **MIX-FREEZE-PAIR**

To review what was learned, use **Mix-Freeze-Pair.** Say "Mix!" and have students stand up and walk around the room. Call out "Freeze!" and wait for everyone to stand still. Then call out "Pair!" and have them link arms with a partner. Call out one of the questions below and have the pairs discuss their answer. After a few minutes of discussion, repeat with the remaining questions.

**What are the 5 senses?**

**Which 3 senses did we use to figure out what was in the Mystery Bags?**

**What 2 senses were not used?**

**Which Mystery Bag was hardest for you to figure out?**

*Science Journal Suggestions*
**Vocabulary:** senses, mystery
**Illustrations:** picture of Mystery Bag with object inside
**Writing:** describe the senses, explain which sense was the most helpful in the Mystery Bag activity, write about a favorite gift

# Materials Check List

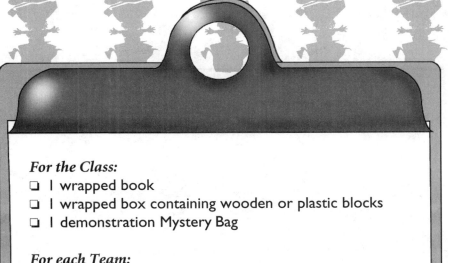

*For the Class:*
- ❏ I wrapped book
- ❏ I wrapped box containing wooden or plastic blocks
- ❏ I demonstration Mystery Bag

*For each Team:*
- ❏ I or more Mystery Bags
- ❏ crayons or colored pencils
- ❏ scissors

*For each Student:*
- ❏ 2 "What's in the Bag?" worksheets

### For Older Students
Older children may enjoy creating their own Mystery Bags. Give each student a lunch bag and a rubber band. Have them place a mystery object inside without the other students seeing it. Team members can trade bags and try to guess what's inside.

### Curriculum Links

**1. Science - Popping popcorn**
Pop popcorn and have students name all the senses they used while enjoying their snack.

**2. Art - Making booklets about the five senses**
Give each team five sheets of paper, each with the name of one sense and a picture of the corresponding body part at the top. For example, the page with "SMELL" would also contain a picture of a nose. In **RoundTable** fashion, have the students draw pictures of things they like to observe using that sense. When the team finishes, everyone should have at least one picture on every page. Staple the pictures together to make team booklets. Display the booklets in a prominent place.

**3. Language Arts - Writing sentences**
Give students a snack (like apples slices) that appeals to all the senses. Have them write a sentence describing what they notice with each sense. For instance, "I hear the apple crunch," or "The apple skin feels smooth." Let them **RoundRobin** their sentences when they finish.

**4. Literature - Listening to My Presents**
Read the flip book *My Presents* to your class. This book by Rod Campbell features flaps that lift to show the contents of wrapped presents.

**5. Art - Making flip-up gift pictures**
Provide a selection of gift wrap and have students each cut out a rectangle of their favorite pattern to represent a gift package. Show them how to glue the top edge of the wrapping paper rectangle to a white piece of drawing paper. Have them flip the rectangle up and draw a picture of a gift they would like to give someone under the wrapping paper. They can flip the wrapping paper "package" down and decorate it with ribbon or a bow. Finally, they can present their "gift" to the person it was created for.

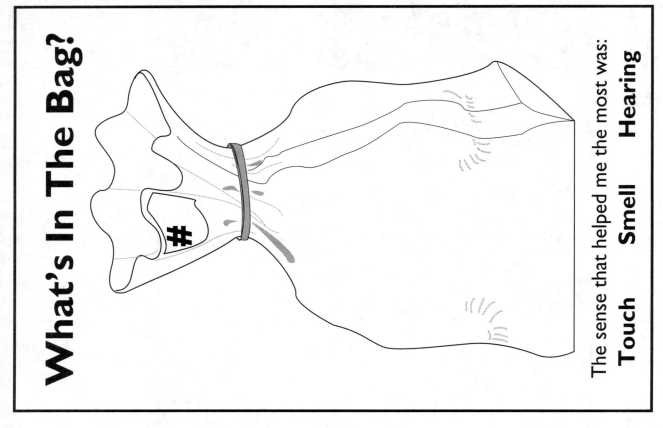

# What's In The Bag?

The sense that helped me the most was:

**Touch     Smell     Hearing**

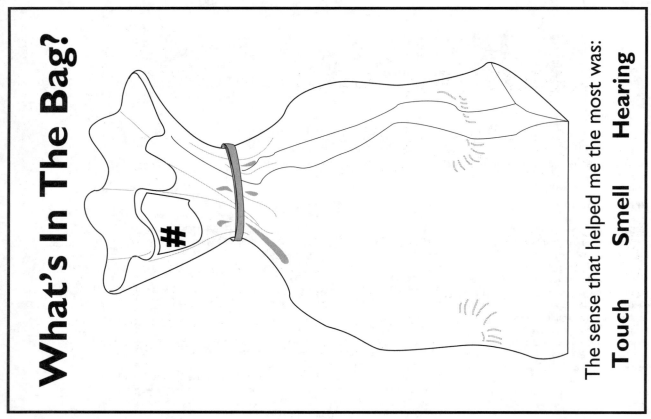

# What's In The Bag?

The sense that helped me the most was:

**Touch     Smell     Hearing**

Students Will...

Listen to book about leaves

Collect leaves

Measure leaves

Observe ways that leaves are alike and different

Graph leaf collection

Process Skills...

Observing

Identifying

Measuring

Predicting

Organizing Data

Communicating

Structures...

Blackboard Share

Class Discussion

Cooperative Play

Numbered Heads Together

Pairs

RallyTable

Team Project

Think-Pair-Share

# Learning with Leaves

**A**fter listening to a book about leaves, your students will go on a leaf hunt. You'll teach them how to identify leaves from different trees. They'll participate in **Numbered Heads Together** to practice identifying various leaves. As a class, they'll graph their favorite leaves and answer questions about their graphs. Finally, they'll measure leaves and make a Leaf Lengths booklet.

Some parts of this lesson can be completed in a learning center. Note the circular "Learning Center" symbol next to these activities.

## 1

### Reading about leaves using TEACHER READS

**Materials for the Class:**
your favorite book about leaves or trees

Read aloud your favorite fiction or nonfiction book about leaves. Some excellent choices are:

*A First Look at Leaves* by Millicent Selsam and Joyce Hunt

*A Tree Is Nice* by Janice Udry

*Red Leaf, Yellow Leaf* by Lois Ehlert

**SAFETY SPOTLIGHT**

Before taking your students on the leaf hunt, ask them not to touch other objects or animals they might find. If your school grounds contain poisonous plants such as poison ivy, make students aware of the location of those plants and tell them not to touch those leaves.

## 2

### Collecting leaves using TEAM PROJECT

**Materials for each Team:**
1 small paper bag

**Materials for the Class:**
at least one tree identification guide book or "T" encyclopedia

Take your class on a leaf hunt. Divide the class into teams of four, and give each team a small paper bag to hold their collection. Walk to an area of the school grounds that has a variety of trees. Tell each person to collect at least five leaves to put in the team's bag. Encourage them to collect different sizes and kinds of leaves. During the leaf hunt, use the tree-identification book or an encyclopedia to identify the trees in the area. Show students pictures of trees in the book and point to the real trees that are similar to them.

The activities which follow work best if your students are able to find at least four different types of leaves. If your school grounds do not contain a variety of trees, ask students to bring leaves from home to contribute to the team collection. Or collect a large bag of leaves yourself and divide them equally between the teams. (If leaves are not readily available, use the Leaf Patterns page to create your own.)

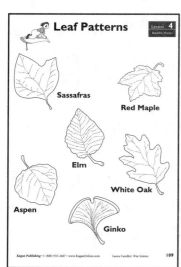

**Leaf Patterns**

Lesson 4

Sassafras

Red Maple

Elm

White Oak

Aspen

Ginko

Kagan Publishing • 1 (800) 933-2667 • www.KaganOnline.com    Laura Candler: Wee Science    109

## 3

### Exploring leaves using COOPERATIVE PLAY

The day after the leaf hunt, seat your students in teams and allow them to spread their leaf collection in front of them. Give them time to play with their leaves in an unstructured manner. Ask them "What do you notice about your leaves?" and let them explore. Encourage them to talk with their team about the things they discover.

## 4

### Discussing leaves using CLASS DISCUSSION

**Materials for the Class:**
overhead transparency of Leaf Patterns page

**Materials for each Team:**
team leaf collection

Now ask students to look at their leaves and find ways that the leaves are alike and different. Discuss color, size, shape, leaf edges, vein patterns, and stems. Explain that leaves which come from the same type of tree may not always be the same size or color, but they will always have the same shape, leaf edges, and vein patterns.

Place the transparency of Leaf Patterns on the overhead projector and point out the characteristics of some common leaves. Ask students if they have any leaves which match those leaf patterns.

## 5

### Identifying leaves using NUMBERED HEADS TOGETHER

Number your students from 1–4 within their teams. You can tape numbered tags on young children to help them remember their number. Choose a leaf that all teams have in their collection. Hold up the leaf and describe its shape, edges, and vein pattern. If you know the name of the tree the leaf came from, identify it by name. Ask team members to put their heads together and try to find a matching leaf within their team collection. Remind them that it does not have to be the same size or color (especially in autumn). When all teams appear to be ready, randomly call out a number from 1–4. Each person whose number was called holds up a matching leaf for the rest of the class to see. Repeat with different leaves.

Make a large grid for graphing the class leaf collection. Draw the graph on the blackboard or butcher paper. If you want a permanent, reusable graph, draw it on plastic. Large white garbage bags work well for this. You can also draw the grid on a vinyl window shade or white table cloth.

Wait until after the leaf hunt to draw the graph. Look at each team's collection to see how many different types of leaves were collected. Draw a grid with 7 rows and enough columns to graph all the different kinds of leaves. For instance, if 6 kinds of leaves are collected, the graph will be 6 blocks wide and 7 blocks high. The blocks should be at least 6" square. Number the left side of the grid from 1 to 7 . Trace one example of each kind of leaf under each column of the graph (see illustration).

If you plan to use the leaves over a long period of time, you may want to preserve them. Melt paraffin wax and dip each leaf in one at a time. Lay the leaves on newspaper to dry. Leaves preserved in this way are easy for children to handle and will not dry out and crumble.

## 6

### *Graphing leaves using* BLACKBOARD SHARE

**Materials for the Class:**
blank grid for graphing leaves

**Materials for each Student:**
favorite leaf
tape

Now ask students which type of leaf they like the best. Tell them that they are going to find out which leaves their classmates like by making a class graph. Have them choose their favorite leaf and place a loop of tape on the back. Allow students to come forward in teams and individually tape their leaves in the columns above the matching leaf tracings. To save time, you can let them complete the graph during the measuring activity. Discuss the graph results at the end of class.

## 7

### *Discussing the graph using* THINK-PAIR-SHARE

When the graph is finished, divide your teams into two sets of pairs. Use **Think-Pair-Share** to discuss questions like the following:

**Which type of leaf do the most students like?**

**How many people like maple leaves (hold up example)?**

**Do more people like maple leaves or elm leaves?**

## Assembling Leaf Booklets using PAIRS

**Materials for each Pair:**
6 leaves
3 copies of Leaf Lengths (Page A)
3 copies of Leaf Lengths (Page B)
1 Our Leaf Lengths booklet cover
pencil
crayons
tape

### Step One: Choosing leaves

In **RoundTable** fashion, have each team member choose three leaves to use in the measurement activity. Tell them to select leaves of different sizes. Have them take turns choosing until everyone has three leaves.

### Step Two: Introducing the activity

Now divide each team into two sets of partners. Give each pair one booklet cover, three copies of each booklet page, a pencil, crayons, tape, and a ruler.

Have your students look at the title on the booklet cover. Tell them that length means how long something is. Then say that they are going to work with their partner to find out the lengths of the six leaves they have between them. First they will glue each leaf onto a box on their booklet pages. Then they will take turns measuring their leaves.

**8 cont.**

Tell each student to write their name in one box on the booklet cover. The boxes have different borders to identify the students' roles. Those who write their names in the butterfly box become Butterflies for this activity. The students who write their names in the ladybug box become Ladybugs. Make sure students know their roles by asking "Who is a Butterfly?" and "Who is a Ladybug?"

### Step Three: Preparing booklet pages

Have your students work together to tape each leaf onto one booklet page. Don't worry if some of the leaves extend outside the box or even outside the page.

Now have your children stack the sheets with Pages A and B alternating. Because of the way students alternate roles, it's very important to alternate the pages throughout the booklet. Check each pair's stack before continuing. Do not staple the pages at this time.

## Measuring leaves using RALLYTABLE

**Materials for each Pair:**
ruler or non-standard measuring implement
pencil
Leaf Lengths Booklet

Consider your students' developmental levels and decide in advance how you want them to measure the leaves in this activity. Provide rulers or non-standard measuring implements for each pair of students.

### Step One: Making predictions
When everyone is ready, have each pair take the first page (Page A) from the stack. Ask your students to look at the leaf and discuss how long they think it is. Tell them that making a prediction means telling what will happen before you do something. Have them discuss their predictions for the lengths of their leaves.

Since the word "prediction" is inside the butterfly box, the Butterflies write the pair's prediction on this page.

### Step Two: Measuring leaves
Now demonstrate how to measure the leaf. Measure from the base of the leaf to its tip, not including the stem.

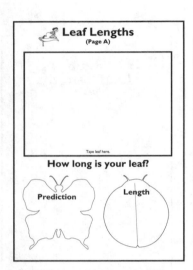

Have the Ladybugs take the measuring implement and measure the leaf on Page A. The Butterflies watch and give help if needed. When both agree on the leaf's length, Ladybugs write the answer in the box on the page.

### Step Three: Completing the booklet
After the first page has been completed, each pair turns the page upside down and places it to the side. They remove Page B from the stack and follow the same sequence of predicting and measuring. However, on this page Ladybugs write the prediction and Butterflies measure. Roles alternate on each page and the answer boxes are coded to provide clues about who predicts and who measures.

When finished, let them color the booklet covers. Assemble the booklet pages in order and staple their covers on top. Display the completed booklets in a prominent location for other students to enjoy.

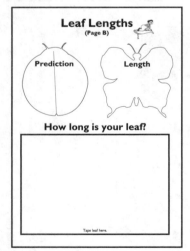

### Science Journal Suggestions
**Vocabulary:** leaf names, prediction, length
**Illustrations:** pictures of leaves, leaf graph
**Writing:** describe the leaf hunt, describe how leaves are alike and different, explain how to measure a leaf, write sentences about the leaf graph

# Materials Check List

*For the Class:*
- ❏ your favorite book about leaves or trees
- ❏ at least one tree identification guide book or "T" encyclopedia
- ❏ overhead transparency of Leaf Patterns page
- ❏ blank grid (for graphing)

*For each Team:*
- ❏ 1 small paper bag
- ❏ team leaf collection

*For each Student:*
- ❏ favorite leaf
- ❏ tape

*For each Pair:*
- ❏ 6 leaves
- ❏ pencil
- ❏ crayons
- ❏ tape
- ❏ 3 copies of Leaf Lengths (Page A)
- ❏ 3 copies of Leaf Lengths (Page B)
- ❏ 1 Our Leaf Lengths booklet cover
- ❏ ruler or nonstandard measuring implement

## For Younger Students

If this lesson is taught in the fall, Kindergarten students may not be ready for the measuring activity. If not, save this part of the lesson for spring. When the new leaves appear, take your class on another leaf collection trip. You can review the concepts learned in the fall before introducing the measurement activity. Another alternative is to preserve the fall leaves by dipping them in melted wax. The preserved leaves will remain usable for many months.

## For Older Students

Older students can record their findings by making bar graphs on paper. Draw a blank grid on paper and duplicate it for each pair of students. Show them how to transfer the results of their leaf graph into bar graph form.

## Curriculum Links

### 1. Art - Making leaf rubbings

Let each student choose his or her favorite leaf. Have them make a leaf rubbing by placing the leaf lower-side up on a tabletop. Then have them cover the leaf with a sheet of thin white paper. They should rub the paper lightly with the side of a crayon, piece of charcoal, or chalk. The shape of the leaf and many of the large veins will appear on the paper.

### 2. Math - Sorting with Venn diagrams

Teach students how to sort using a Venn diagram. Have each person choose a leaf. Overlap two hula-hoops or loops of yarn on the floor. Label the circles with leaf characteristics and let each person place his or her leaf in the correct spot

### 3. Language Arts - Writing the life story of a leaf

Ask students to imagine themselves as a leaf unfolding from a bud in spring. Then talk them through the heat of summer and the color changes of fall. Finally, have them write a story about their imagined life as a leaf. Young children can tell their stories with pictures.

# Our Leaf Lengths

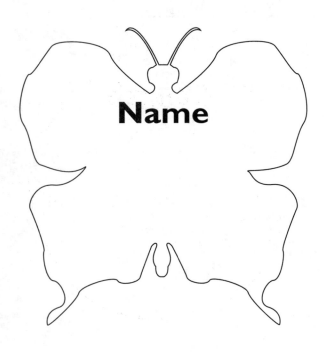

**Name**

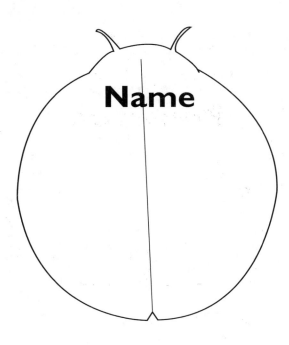

**Name**

Laura Candler: *Wee Science*     ***Kagan Publishing*** • 1 (800) 933-2667 • www.KaganOnline.com

# Leaf Lengths
## (Page A)

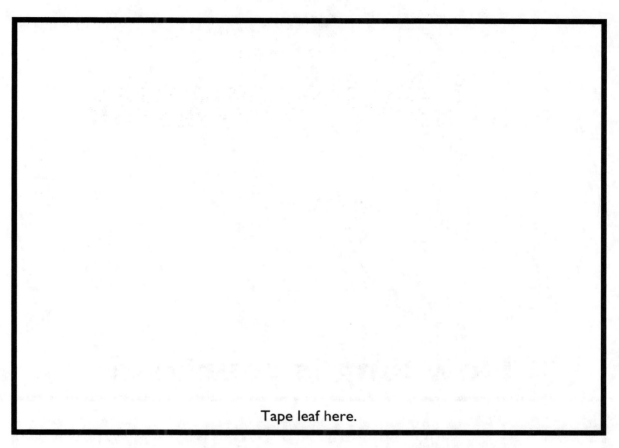

Tape leaf here.

# How long is your leaf?

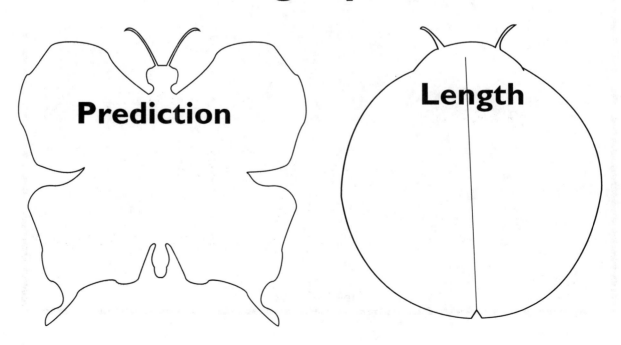

Prediction

Length

# Leaf Lengths
## (Page B)

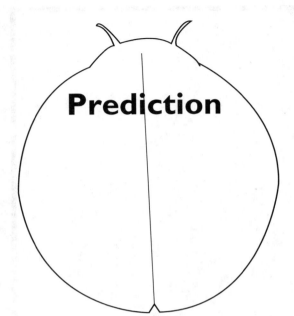

**Prediction**

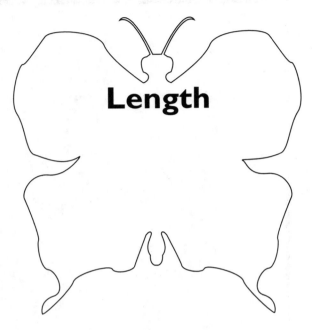

**Length**

## How long is your leaf?

Tape leaf here.

# Leaf Patterns

Sassafras

Red Maple

Elm

White Oak

Aspen

Ginko

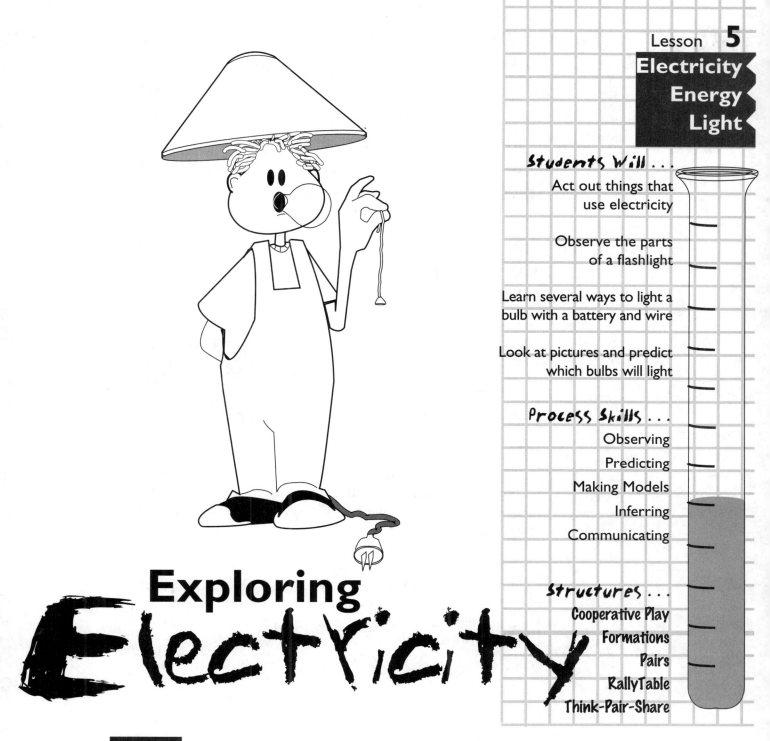

## Exploring Electricity

**Students Will...**

Act out things that use electricity

Observe the parts of a flashlight

Learn several ways to light a bulb with a battery and wire

Look at pictures and predict which bulbs will light

**Process Skills...**

Observing
Predicting
Making Models
Inferring
Communicating

**Structures...**

Cooperative Play
Formations
Pairs
RallyTable
Think-Pair-Share

**E**lectricity seems almost magical to young children. They flip a switch and a toy begins talking or a light turns on. They know that some items must have a battery to work, but they have no understanding of how electricity must follow a path, or circuit, in order to make that object work.

Your students will begin this lesson by acting out items that use electricity, letting other teams guess the object they are portraying. Then they will observe the parts of a flashlight to see how it works. Next, they will work in pairs to light a bulb with a battery and wire. Finally, they will look at pictures of batteries and bulbs and will try to predict which bulbs will light before testing their ideas.

 Some parts of the lesson can be completed in a learning center. Note the circular "Learning Center" symbol next to these activities.

## I

### *Discussing electricity using* THINK-PAIR-SHARE

Write the word electricity on the board and pronounce it for your students. Ask them if they know what electricity is. Have them think about their answer, then pair with their partner to discuss their ideas. Finally, call on several students to share their ideas with the class.

The simplest explanation is that electricity is energy that gives "power" to many things to make them work. You can point out that people get their energy by eating food; some things get their energy from electricity. Electricity can come from electrical outlets or batteries.

***Prepare Electrical Item Cards***
Cut apart both sets of Electrical Items cards. Choose the items you want your students to act out. You'll need at least one card per team. Place the cards in a box or brown paper bag so that one student from each team will be able to draw one out.

## 2

### *Acting out electrical items using* FORMATIONS

**Materials for the Class:**
I set of Electrical Item Cards in a box or bag

### *Step One: Introducing the activity*
Tell your students that they are going to play a game in which each team acts out something that uses electricity. The rest of the class will have to try to figure out what the object is.

### *Step Two: Modeling a formation*
Ask one team to help you show the class what to do. Let one teammate draw a card from the bag and secretly show it to you. Huddle together with the team and explain what each person needs to do to act out the object. In a team of four, three students can act out the object and one student can be the person using the object. For instance, if "Popcorn Popper" was chosen, three students could act out the actual popper and one person could pretend to plug it and pour in the popcorn. Encourage students to use sound effects. After the team acts out the object for a few seconds, have the other teams discuss what they think the object is. If they have trouble, read out all the possible choices. Call on one person from each team to tell the team's guess.

### *Step Three: Drawing a card*
Now call on one person from each team to come forward and draw out the name of one item. If your students are non-readers, whisper the name of the object to each person as they draw out the card.

(continued on page 114)

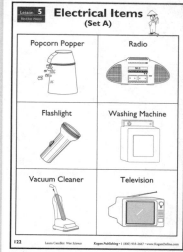

Lesson 5
**Electrical Items**
(Set A)

Popcorn Popper | Radio
Flashlight | Washing Machine
Vacuum Cleaner | Television

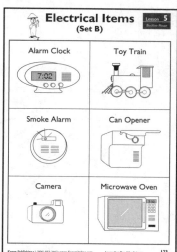

**Electrical Items**
(Set B)
Lesson 5

Alarm Clock | Toy Train
Smoke Alarm | Can Opener
Camera | Microwave Oven

**2 cont.**

### Acting out electrical items (continued from page 113)

#### Step Four: Practicing formations
Let each team find a place in the classroom to practice their formation. With very young children, you may have to help each team individually. Plan the practice session to take place at a learning center or during a seatwork activity. Call each team to an open location in the room to work with you on their formation.

#### Step Five: Showing formations
When all teams have had a chance to practice, let them present their formations to the class. Randomly call on teams, one at a time, to act out their electrical objects in front of the class.

#### Step Six: Guessing formations
After each team has presented its formation, give the other teams a chance to discuss what they think the object is. Once again, read the entire list of electrical objects if they are having a difficult time guessing. Call on one member of each team to make their team's guess.

SAFETY

SPOTLIGHT

Occasionally a wire will get hot when students are experimenting with batteries. This happens when the battery is accidentally short-circuited by touching the wire to both ends of the battery without the bulb in between. Tell students to notice how the wire feels at all times. If it seems to get a little warm they should immediately drop the wire and tell you. Have them show you what they did so they will understand what caused the problem.

Make sure students understand the difference between experimenting with batteries and playing with electrical outlets. *Tell them that they should never stick wires of any kind into electrical outlets because this kind of electricity is very powerful.* They could be seriously injured by putting objects into outlets.

**3**

### *Showing the parts of a flashlight*
### *using* **TEACHER DEMONSTRATES**

**Materials for the Class:**
1 flashlight

Now tell your students that you are going to show them how one of the objects gets its energy. Hold up a flashlight and turn it on to show that it works. Then turn it off and open the end where the batteries are stored. Take out the batteries, close the flashlight, and try to turn it on. Ask students why they don't think it works anymore. Tell them that the batteries make electricity for the flashlight. The batteries are connected by wires to the bulb. The electricity goes through the wires to the bulb to make it light. Without the batteries, the lightbulb doesn't have any energy to light up.

Tell students that they will be learning about electricity by studying batteries. This would be a good time to discuss electricity safety. Explain that there are two types of electricity: electricity from batteries and electricity from electrical outlets. Batteries are perfectly safe to experiment with, but electrical outlets are not. Make sure they understand that they should never place any object into an electrical outlet; they could be seriously injured.

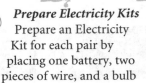

***Prepare Electricity Kits***
Prepare an Electricity
Kit for each pair by
placing one battery, two
pieces of wire, and a bulb
in a ziptop baggie. These materials
do not have to be ordered from
a science catalog; they may be
purchased at any electronics store
such as Radio Shack.

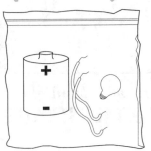

**Materials For each Kit:**
- I D-cell battery
- 2 ten-inch pieces of insulated wire
- I flashlight bulb
- I piece of tissue paper *or*
  - I film canister filled with cotton
- I ziptop baggie

You'll need one D-cell battery for each kit. Inexpensive general purpose batteries are preferable to the stronger alkaline batteries. You'll also need two 10-inch pieces of insulated solid wire per kit. The exact diameter is not important, but 20- gauge wire works well. Use scissors or wire strippers to remove about an inch of insulation from both ends of each piece of wire. Finally, you'll need a flashlight bulb for each kit. Wrap each bulb in tissue paper or put it in a film canister stuffed with cotton before placing it in the kit. Be sure to buy a few extra bulbs since some will break despite these precautions.

**4**

### Exploring materials using COOPERATIVE PLAY

**Materials for each Pair:**
I Electricity Kit prepared earlier
masking tape

Give each pair of students one Electricity Kit prepared earlier. Allow them to take out the materials. Caution them to be careful not to drop the bulb since it is made of glass and will break easily.

Give your students a chance to play with the materials in an unstructured manner for a short time. Then challenge them to use the battery and wire to make the bulb light. Give them a few minutes to play with the materials to see if they can accomplish this on their own. Tell them that if the wire becomes warm, they should drop it immediately and let you know.

Most students won't figure out how to light the bulb, but this exploration period is important. Your children will be more prepared to watch you demonstrate how to light the bulb if they have had a chance to try on their own first.

*Prepare Demonstration Materials*
Make a large set of demonstration materials. Follow the directions for each item below:

**bulb** Use a household lightbulb, any wattage.

**wire** Cut two 3" x 24" long strips of aluminum foil. Roll the foil lengthwise to make two large "wires."

**battery** Cover an empty oatmeal box with aluminum foil to represent a battery. Before you cover it, however, make a slight "bump" on one end for the positive terminal of the battery. To do this, roll several sheets of newspaper into a tube and then around in a spiral to form a doughnut shape. Tape this "doughnut" on top of the oatmeal box. Cover the entire box with aluminum foil. Use a magic marker to make a large plus sign on the positive end and a minus sign on the other end.

**Materials For the Bulb:**
household lightbulb

**Materials For the Wire:**
aluminum foil

**Materials For the Battery:**
oatmeal box
tape
newspaper
aluminum foil
magic marker

**oatmeal box**     **aluminum foil strips**      **household bulb**

**5**

## Lighting a bulb using PAIRS

**Materials for the Class:**
1 set of demonstration materials prepared earlier
1 copy of Simple Ways to Light a Bulb worksheet

### Step One: Learning the first method
Use the worksheet "Simple Ways to Light a Bulb" to guide you in demonstrating how to light the bulb. You may draw these illustrations on the board or make a transparency of the worksheet if you wish.

Ask several students to come forward to help hold the demonstration materials. Hold up the large "battery" and point to the end with the plus sign. Tell your class that this is called the **positive** end of the battery. They can tell which end is the positive end because it has a plus sign and a small bump on the end. Have them find the positive end of their own battery before going on. Now show them the end with the minus sign and tell them that it is the **negative** end and is flat. Some batteries do not have the plus and minus sign, but they can always tell which end is which by the bump on one end.

(continued on page 118)

### *Lighting a bulb* (continued from page 117)

Now use the large battery, one aluminum foil "wire," and the household bulb to demonstrate the first method of lighting a bulb. Show your student volunteers how to hold the materials as pictured in illustration #1. Tell them that the household bulb will not light since you are not using a real bulb, but their bulbs will light if they set up their materials in the same way.

Give each pair time to try to light their bulb using one piece of wire. Move from team to team to show them how if they are having difficulty.

**Step Two: Learning the second method**
After everyone is successful, demonstrate the method shown in illustration #2. The technique is almost the same except the bulb is placed on the negative end of the battery. Let everyone try this method.

**Step Three: Learning the third method**
The third method is the most difficult because it involves holding two pieces of wire. You may want students to tape the wires to the batteries so that their hands will be free to touch the wires to the bulb correctly. Make sure that they understand that one wire must touch the *side* of the bulb and the other must touch the *bottom* of the bulb. If both wires touch the same area of the bulb it will not light and the wire will get hot very quickly.

Point out that in all three examples the materials must join together to make a complete path for the electricity. If everything isn't touching, the bulb won't light. If you feel your students are ready, introduce the word ***circuit*** as the path that electricity must go through to light the bulb.

**Step Four: Practicing**
After demonstrating all three methods, give your students additional time to play with the materials on their own. Ask them to go back and try all three ways of lighting the bulb one more time. Also, tell them to notice the things they do that *don't* make the bulb light.

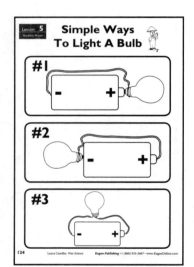

**6**

## Checking for understanding using RALLYTABLE

**Materials for each Pair:**
1 copy of Which Bulb Will Light? worksheet
1 Electricity Kit
1 pencil
1 yellow crayon
1 black crayon

### Step One: Explaining the worksheet
Distribute the materials to each pair of students. Give one person in each pair the worksheet and pencil. Give their partner the Electricity Kit along with the yellow and black crayons. Tell them that they are going to work together to make predictions about which bulbs on the worksheet will light.

### Step Two: Making the first prediction
Tell everyone to look closely at the first picture and discuss with their partner whether or not that bulb will light. Write the word prediction on the board and tell your children that making a prediction means guessing what will happen before you do something.

After the two students have discussed their prediction for the first picture, have the person with the pencil circle "yes" or "no."

### Step Three: Testing predictions
Now have them work together to test the first prediction. Tell them to place their battery, bulb, and wire exactly as shown in the picture. Walk around the room to make sure they are setting up their materials properly.

(continued on page 120)

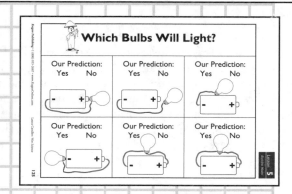

## 6 cont.

### *Checking for understanding* (continued from page 119)

#### Step Four: Recording results
They should discover that the bulb in picture #1 will light. Now tell them that if the bulb lights, the person with the yellow crayon colors the bulb yellow. If the bulb does not light, the same person colors the bulb black.

#### Step Five: Finishing the worksheet
After completing the first example, the two students switch materials. After the **Pair Discussion** about the second picture, the person who colored the bulb now circles the prediction. After testing their prediction, their partner colors the bulb either yellow or black. Students switch roles for each picture as they complete the rest of the worksheet.

### *Science Journal Suggestions*
**Vocabulary:** electricity, battery, wire, bulb, circuit, prediction
**Illustrations:** ways to light a bulb, things that use electricity
**Writing:** describing how to make a bulb light, listing things that use electricity, naming electricity safety rules

### *For Younger Students*
Kindergarten teachers may want to modify the **Formations** activity if it is too difficult for their students. Instead of having teams portray the electrical items, the teacher can form the objects with the help of a few students. The rest of the students **Think-Pair-Share** the name of that electrical item. Teachers can vary the activity further by pantomiming the object's use instead of acting out the object itself. For instance, they can make ironing motions or pretend to dry their hair. As before, the members of the class **Think-Pair-Share** the name of the object.

# Materials Check List

**For each Electricity Kit:**
- ❏ 1 D-cell battery
- ❏ 1 flashlight bulb
- ❏ 1 piece tissue paper *or* 1 film canister filled with cotton
- ❏ 2 ten-inch pieces insulated wire
- ❏ 1 ziptop baggie

**For Demonstration Materials:**
- ❏ household lightbulb
- ❏ oatmeal box
- ❏ newspaper
- ❏ aluminum foil
- ❏ tape
- ❏ magic marker

**For the Class:**
- ❏ 1 set of Electrical Item Cards in a box or bag
- ❏ 1 flashlight
- ❏ 1 set of Demonstration Materials
- ❏ 1 copy of Simple Ways to Light a Bulb worksheet

**For each Pair:**
- ❏ 1 Electricity Kit
- ❏ 1 pencil
- ❏ 1 black crayon
- ❏ masking tape
- ❏ 1 yellow crayon
- ❏ 1 copy of Which Bulb Will Light? worksheet

## Curriculum Links

**1. Art - Making collages**
Have students use magazines to cut out pictures of things that use electricity. Let each team make a collage of their pictures.

**2. Science - Listing ways to conserve electricity**
Explain to your students the importance of not wasting electricity. Have them **RoundRobin** ways that they can save electricity at home and at school. Let them illustrate their ideas on a poster.

**3. Language Arts - Writing about life without electricity**
Discuss with your class how our lives would be different without electricity. Then have students write a story about living one day without electricity. Very young children can tell their stories in picture form.

# Electrical Items
## (Set A)

| | |
|---|---|
| **Popcorn Popper**  | **Radio** 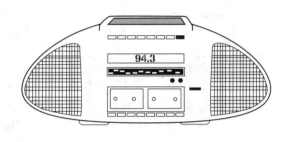 |
| **Flashlight**  | **Washing Machine** 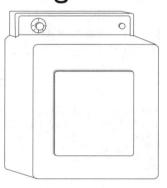 |
| **Vacuum Cleaner** 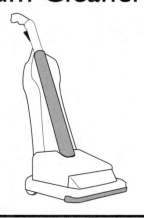 | **Television** 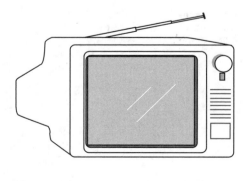 |

# Electrical Items
## (Set B)

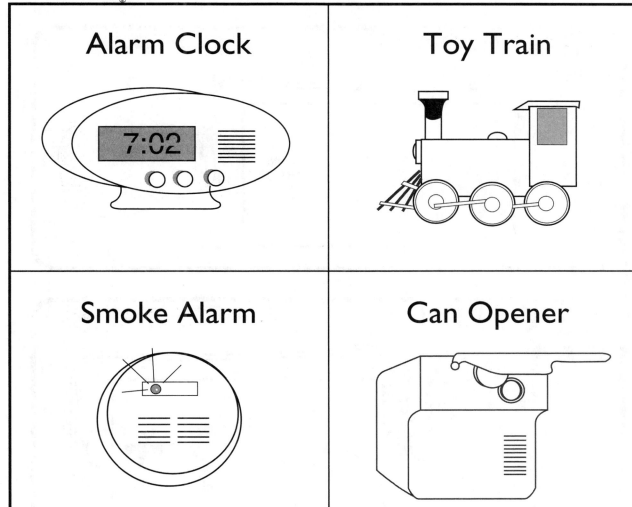

**Alarm Clock**

**Toy Train**

**Smoke Alarm**

**Can Opener**

**Camera**

**Microwave Oven**

# Simple Ways To Light A Bulb

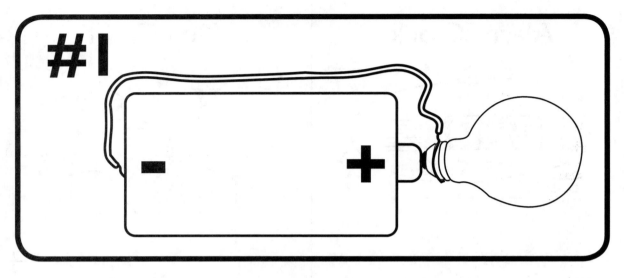

**#1**

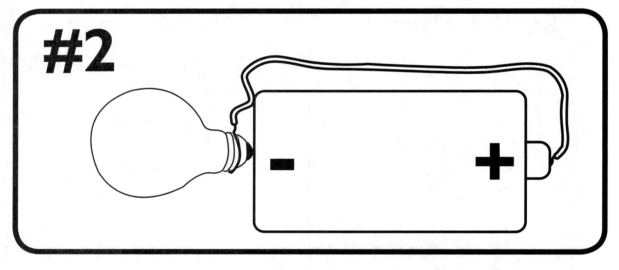

**#2**

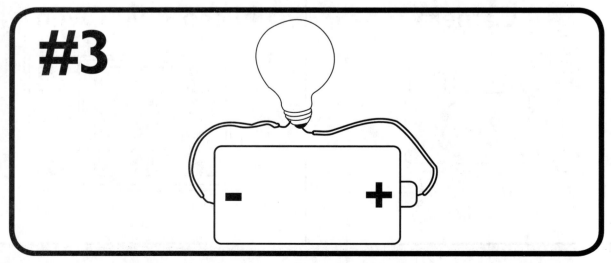

**#3**

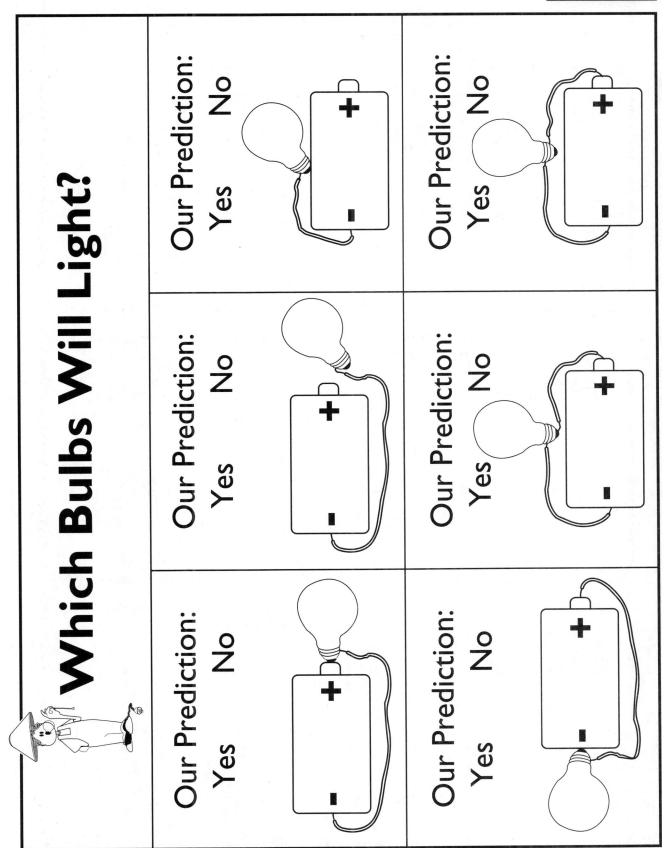

# Which Bulbs Will Light?

Our Prediction: Yes No

Our Prediction: Yes No

Our Prediction: Yes No

Our Prediction: Yes No

Our Prediction: Yes No

Our Prediction: Yes No

**Students Will . . .**

Discuss why rain forests are important

Listen to *The Great Kapok Tree* by Lynne Cherry

Color location of rain forests on world map

Sort pictures of rain forest animals using Venn diagrams

Taste rain forest foods

Hunt for rain forest products at home

**Process Skills . . .**

Observing

Identifying

Classifying

Predicting

Organizing Data

Communicating

**Structures . . .**

Cooperative Play

Mix-Freeze-Pair

Pairs

RallyTable

RoundTable

Team Project

Think-Pair-Share

# Wonders of the Rain Forest

e may live thousands of miles from the nearest tropical rain forests, yet these areas impact our lives greatly. The trees provide a big portion of the earth's oxygen and are home to thousands of plant and animal species. Because the tropics are so fascinating, even young children can develop an appreciation for rain forests.

You'll begin the lesson by reading *The Great Kapok Tree,* a story of a huge tree in the tropical rain forest. After listening to the book, your students will color the location of the rain forests on a simple world map. They will sort rain forest animal pictures using Venn diagrams. Finally, they will taste foods from the rain forest and will hunt for rain forest products at home.

 Some parts of this lesson can be completed in a learning center. Note the circular "Learning Center" symbol next to these activities.

## 1

### *Introducing the tropical rain forest* *using* TEACHER TALK

**Materials for the Class:**
*The Great Kapok Tree* by Lynne Cherry
1 globe

Introduce your students to the tropical rain forest by showing them the cover of *The Great Kapok Tree.* Say:

*For the next few days we will be learning about the tropical rain forest, a place some people call the jungle. In a few minutes I will read you the story of* The Great Kapok Tree *which is about a huge tree in the tropical rain forest.*

*But first I want to tell you a little about rain forests. Let me show you where tropical rain forests grow on the Earth.(On the globe, point to the areas of the continents around the equator.) These forests are hot and wet all year long. Lots of colorful animals, birds, and insects live in the rain forest. Many giant trees and plants grow there. The trees and plants make oxygen which we need to breathe. We get many important medicines and lots of delicious foods from the tropical rain forest.*

*The problem is that people are cutting down these beautiful forests. They want to use the wood from the giant trees. They also want to make room for farmland. One day all the tropical rain forests may be gone.*

**2**

## Making predictions using THINK-PAIR-SHARE

Now read *The Great Kapok Tree* aloud. Stop in several places and have students **Think-Pair-Share** their predictions about what will happen next.

### Prepare Rain Forest Animal Cards

Duplicate one two-page set of Rain Forest Animal Cards for each pair of students in your class. If you want to make permanent sets, cut the cards apart and color them using the pictures on the inside cover of *The Great Kapok Tree* as a guide. Laminate the cards so that they can withstand handling and be used again for other activities. Store each set of 16 cards in a zip-top bag.

**3**

## Exploring animal pictures using COOPERATIVE PLAY

**Materials for the Class:**
1 or more copies of *The Great Kapok Tree* by Lynne Cherry

**Materials for each Pair:**
1 set of 16 Rain Forest Animal Cards
scissors
crayons or colored pencils

If you only have one copy of *The Great Kapok Tree,* this lesson will need to be completed at a learning center. Give each pair of students one set of Rain Forest Animal Cards. Tell your students that these are some of the many rain forest animals they learned about in the story. Explain that will each cut apart and color one page of animals, but they will share the set of 16 cards during the rest of the lesson. Let them look at the illustrations on the inside cover of *The Great Kapok Tree* so they can color the pictures accurately. You may want to color a sample set of cards and leave them at a learning center for your children to use as a guide.

After they have finished, allow them to spread all the pictures out before them and play with them in an unstructured manner for a few minutes.

**4**

## *Sequencing pictures using* RALLYTABLE

**Materials for each Pair:**
1 set of 16 Rain Forest Animal Cards

### Step One: Identifying animals
Give each pair of students one set of Animal Cards. Hold up one picture at a time and pronounce the name of the animal. Have your students point to their matching card and repeat the animal's name.

### Step Two: Dividing animal cards
Next, have your students turn their cards upside down and mix them up. Now ask them to each take *eight* of the cards without looking at them. As soon as the cards are divided, tell them to turn the cards face up and look at them carefully.

### Step Three: Listening and sequencing
Now read *The Great Kapok Tree* aloud again. As you name each animal in the story, pause long enough for your students to find the matching animal card. The two students will form a row of cards *face up* in sequence. In each pair, whoever has the card should add it to the row. Only eleven of the cards will be used.

## Face-Up Illustrations

|  |  |  |  |  |  |  |  |  |  |  |
|---|---|---|---|---|---|---|---|---|---|---|
| Boa Constrictor | Bee | Monkey | Toucan | Macaw | Cock-of-the-Rock | Tree Frog | Jaguar | Tree Porcupine | Anteater | Sloth |

**Make Transparency**
Make a transparency or poster of the Rain Forests of the Earth worksheet. Leave it blank so that you can demonstrate how to color the various areas.

**5**

## Coloring rain forests using PAIRS

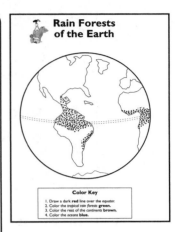

**Rain Forests of the Earth**

**Color Key**
1. Draw a dark **red** line over the equator.
2. Color the tropical rain forests **green**.
3. Color the rest of the continents **brown**.
4. Color the oceans **blue**.

**Materials for the Class:**
1 globe
transparency or poster of Rain Forests of the Earth worksheet

**Materials for each Student:**
1 Rain Forests of the Earth worksheet

**Materials for each Pair:**
1 box of crayons

In this activity, each student will color his or her own worksheet. However, they will work with their partner to make sure they both color the correct areas.

Distribute the worksheets and crayons. Show your students the location of the rain forest on the globe and also on the inside cover of *The Great Kapok Tree.* Show the transparency or poster and demonstrate how to color the worksheet properly. The dot pattern on the worksheet indicates tropical rain forests. Have your students follow the directions in the color key, stopping to check with their partner after each step is completed.

**6**

## Classifying animals by one characteristic using RALLYTABLE

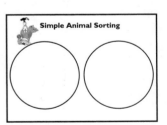

**Simple Animal Sorting**

**Materials for each Pair:**
1 set of 16 Rain Forest Animal Cards
1 Simple Animal Sorting worksheet

### Step One: Discussing animal characteristics
Give each pair one set of 16 animal cards and one Simple Animal Sorting worksheet. Ask your students to look at all their animals and to think about how the animals are alike and different. Ask them to talk with their partner about one way they could divide the animal pictures into just two piles. Call on a few students to give some ideas. Some examples might be: insects in one pile and everything else in the other, mammals in one pile and all others in the other, or animals that can fly in one pile and animals that can't in the other.

(continued on page 132)

*Classifying animals* (continued from page 131)

Write the word **attribute** on the board. Tell the class that they have just named "attributes" of rain forest animals. Attributes are ways animals are alike and different.

*Step Two: Sorting animal cards*
Have your students turn the cards upside down, mix them up, and each take eight of them. Ask them to turn the cards face up for the sorting activity.

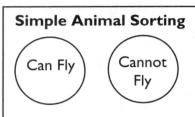

**Simple Animal Sorting**

Can Fly    Cannot Fly

Now choose one attribute such as "can fly" and tell your students to take turns placing their cards into one circle or the other on their worksheet to divide them. Monitor their work to make sure they are taking turns and placing their cards correctly.

Lead them through several more examples. Try categories like "birds" and "not birds" or "has scaly skin" and "does not have scaly skin." Discuss the word "not" as a way of grouping everything that doesn't go into the first circle.

Now ask your students to work with their partner to sort the animals in their own way. Have them divide the animals into two piles and then ask their teammates to figure out how the cards are divided.

**7**

*Introducing Venn diagrams using* **THINK-PAIR-SHARE**

**Materials for the Class:**
1 set of 16 Rain Forest Animal Cards
2 hula hoops (different colors if possible)
4 sheets of construction paper (9" x 12")
marker

*Step One: Getting started*
Have the class form a large circle with everyone sitting next to their partner. Designate one person in each pair as the "A" partner and one person as the "B" partner. Give each pair one animal card and ask them to place it on the floor in front of them.

*Step Two: Sorting by two attributes*
Place the two hula hoops beside each other in the center of the circle. The hoops should be close but *not overlapping*. Tell the class that you will use the hula hoops to sort by *two* attributes at a time.

(continued on page 133)

### *Introducing Venn diagrams* (continued from page 132)

Write the words "Can Fly" on a sheet of construction paper and hold it up for your students to see. Ask each pair to look at their animal picture and *think* about whether or not their animal flies. Have them *pair* and discuss this question. For the *sharing* activity say, "If your animal flies, I want Partner A to hold it up for the class to see." Check for correctness.

Now write the words "Has a Tail" on another sheet of construction paper. Ask students to *think,* then *pair* to discuss whether or not their animal has a tail. Have Partner B hold up the card if they agree that the animal has a tail.

#### *Step Three: Making the transition*
Place the attribute labels inside the hula hoops. Tell the students that in a few minutes they will place the animals with a tail in one circle and the animals that can fly in the other. Animals that don't have either attribute go outside the circles.

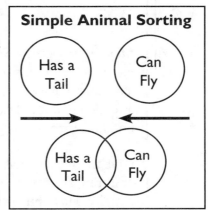

Hold up one of the bird pictures. Ask students to **Think-Pair-Share** where they would put the picture since it has both attributes. Some students may say to put it in either place, but hopefully some will say to put the picture in the middle.

At this point tell students that you have an even better idea. Slide the hula hoops together so that they are now overlapping. Tell them that any picture with both attributes goes in the middle. Explain that the two overlapping circles are called a **Venn diagram.** Venn diagrams are used for sorting pictures, numbers, or objects.

**7 cont.**

#### *Step Four: Placing pictures*
Now ask students to *think* about where they will place their pictures on the Venn diagram. Have them *pair* to discuss their ideas. When it's time to *share* ideas, have Partner A come forward and place their picture in the correct location.

When all the pictures are in place, ask your students to look at all the pictures. Have them **Think-Pair-Share** whether all the pictures are in the correct locations. Move any pictures that are not placed correctly.

#### *Step Five: Repeating activity*
Now collect the animal cards and give every pair a different picture. Repeat the entire **Think-Pair-Share** activity using the attributes of "Has Legs" and "Has Scaly Skin."

**8**

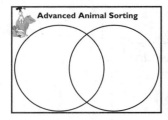

Advanced Animal Sorting

## *Classifying with Venn diagrams*
## *using* RALLYTABLE

**Materials for each Pair:**
1 set of 16 Rain Forest Animal Cards
1 Advanced Animal Sorting worksheet
pencil

### Step One:  Getting Started
Now send students back to their seats to practice Venn diagrams with
a partner. Give each pair one Advanced Animal Sorting Worksheet
and a set of animal cards. Have them turn the sixteen cards face down
and take turns choosing cards until they each have eight.

Give them two attributes to use in sorting their pictures. For young
children, start with two of the attributes you used in the hula hoop
activity. Have one person write the attribute titles in the circles.
Consider the following combinations:

> **Insects and Has Green Coloring**
> **Reptiles and Has Stripes**
> **Has a Tail and Mammals**
> **Has Stripes and Can Fly**
> **Has Fur and Has Spots**
> **Has 4 Legs and Has Fur**

### Step Two:  Sorting animal pictures
Now have your students take turns placing their animal pictures
in the correct place on their Venn diagrams. Encourage them to
discuss each card's placement with their partner. When they are
finished, discuss the results with them. Then have them erase the
attribute titles and write in new ones.

***Prepare Food Samples***
Collect a variety of foods grown in the rain forest for your students to sample.
Cut the foods into bite-sized pieces so that everyone will be able to have a sample.
Some tasty food choices are: bananas, Brazil nuts, cashews, cocoa, pineapple, kiwi,
peanuts, and chewing gum.

## 9

### *Tasting foods using* INDIVIDUALS OBSERVE

**Materials for each Student:**
samples of rain forest foods

Explain to your students that many **products,** or things we
buy, come from the rain forest. Say that foods are examples
of products. Give each person a few bite-sized pieces of rain
forest foods to taste.

Ask them to think about how the foods smell and feel in their
mouths also. Some foods feel smooth, others are chewy, and
others are mushy.

## 10

### *Describing favorite foods using* ROUNDROBIN

After everyone has had a chance to taste the
foods, have them **RoundRobin** which of the foods was
their favorite. On each team, have Person #1 start by
naming his or her favorite food and telling why they
liked it. Then have Person #2, #3, and #4 continue in
the same fashion.

11

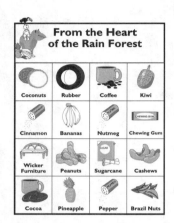

### From the Heart of the Rain Forest

| | | | |
|---|---|---|---|
| Coconuts | Rubber | Coffee | Kiwi |
| Cinnamon | Bananas | Nutmeg | Chewing Gum |
| Wicker Furniture | Peanuts | Sugarcane | Cashews |
| Cocoa | Pineapple | Pepper | Brazil Nuts |

Dear Parents,

We have been studying tropical rain forests for the past few days. Did you know that many products we buy come from the rain forest?

Please take a few minutes to hunt with your child for the items on the worksheet. Have your child color in any products you find. If possible, let your child bring one or more of the products to share with the class.

Have your child return the worksheet and any rain forest items on the due date given below. Thank you!

Sincerely,

Due Date: _____

## Discovering rain forest products using TEAM PROJECT

**Materials for each Student:**
1 copy of From the Heart of the Rain Forest worksheet
1 copy of the letter to parents

**Materials for each Team:**
1 copy of From the Heart of the Rain Forest worksheet
1 box of crayons

### Step One: Introducing the scavenger hunt
Now give each person one copy of the worksheet entitled "From the Heart of the Rain Forest" and one copy of the letter to parents. Ask them if they have ever heard of a scavenger hunt. Explain that it means to try to find things on a list. Tell them that they are going to take the worksheet home and hunt for as many of the products as possible. Tell them to ask an adult to help them look for the things shown on their worksheet. Have them color in any items that they find in their home. Ask them to bring in examples of some of the products if they can.

*(Note: All of the products on the worksheet can be found in the rain forest; however, the rain forest is not a major producer of most items. Many products were originally discovered in the rain forest but are now commercially grown on large farms.)*

### Step Two: Compiling results
When students return the next day with their worksheets and products, tell them that they are going to see how many items their team found together. Give them a few minutes to look at all the rain forest products brought in by their teammates.

(continued on page 137)

### Discovering rain forest products (continued from page 136)

Give each team a blank copy of "From the Heart of the Rain Forest." In **RoundTable** fashion, have the students color in all the items they found at home, even if they didn't bring the items to school. Assign each student the following crayon colors by number:

| | |
|---|---|
| **Person #1 - Green** | **Person #3 - Orange** |
| **Person #2 - Blue** | **Person #4 - Red** |

Have Person #1 take the blank team copy of the worksheet and color in green *one item* that he or she found at home. Then ask them to pass the worksheet to Person #2 who colors in blue *one item* found at home. The students continue passing and coloring until they finish coloring all items or can't color any more.

Display the completed team worksheets in a prominent location along with the product samples brought in by students.

**12**

### Reviewing the wonders of the rain forest using MIX-FREEZE-PAIR

Use **Mix-Freeze-Pair** to review concepts learned during this lesson. Say "Mix!" and have students walk quietly around the room, mixing with other classmates. Call out "Freeze!" and have them stand still. When you say "Pair!" they link arms with a partner. Then ask them to discuss one of the questions below with that person. Call on several students to share their responses with the class.

> **Would you like to visit a tropical rain forest? Why or why not?**
>
> **How do you think it would feel to be in a rain forest?**
>
> **Why are rain forests important?**
>
> **Why are people cutting down rain forests?**
>
> **What are some animals of the rain forest?**
>
> **What are some products from the rain forest?**

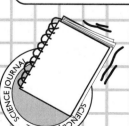

**Science Journal Suggestions**
**Vocabulary:** tropical rain forest, product, Venn diagram, equator
**Illustrations:** rain forest animals and products
**Writing:** reasons for saving the rain forest, stories about animals of the rain forest, descriptions of rain forest products, reasons why they would or would not like to visit a tropical rain forest

# Materials Check List

**For the Class:**
- ❏ *The Great Kapok Tree* by Lynne Cherry
- ❏ 1 transparency or poster of Rain Forests of the Earth
- ❏ 1 set of 16 Rain Forest Animal Cards
- ❏ 2 hula hoops (different colors if possible)
- ❏ 4 sheets of construction paper (9"x12")
- ❏ marker
- ❏ 1 globe

**For each Pair:**
- ❏ 1 set of 16 Rain Forest Animal Cards
- ❏ 1 Simple Animal Sorting worksheet
- ❏ 1 Advanced Animal Sorting worksheet
- ❏ scissors
- ❏ crayons or colored pencils
- ❏ pencil

**For each Team:**
- ❏ 1 copy of the From the Heart of the Rain Forest worksheet
- ❏ 1 box of crayons

**For each Student:**
- ❏ 1 Rain Forests of the Earth worksheet
- ❏ samples of rain forest foods
- ❏ 1 copy of the letter to parents
- ❏ 1 copy of the From the Heart of the Rain Forest worksheet

## Curriculum Links

**1. Literature - Reading about the rain forest**
Read *Welcome to the Green House* aloud to your class. This book by Jane Yolen reads like poetry and gives a vivid description of the world of the rain forest. Another excellent book is *Rain Forest Secrets* by Arthur Dorros. This nonfiction book gives facts and information in an easy-to-read form.

**2. Language Arts - Writing letters**
To find out what they can do to save the rain forest, have students write to:

The Children's Rain Forest
P.O. Box 936
Lewiston, ME 04240

**3. Art - Making a rain forest mural**
Tear off a long sheet of white butcher paper. Divide it into sections, one for each team. Using books about the rain forest for illustration ideas, allow teams to paint large green trees and plants for a background. Then have them paint colorful birds, insects, reptiles, and mammals in the trees.

**4. Math - Graphing favorite rain forest foods**
After students sample foods from the rain forest, have students make a class bar graph of their favorite foods.

# Rain Forest Animal Cards (Set A)

Bee

Cock-of-the-Rock

Scarlet Macaw

Toucan

Tree Frog

Monkey

Jaguar

Boa Constrictor

# Rain Forest Animal Cards (Set B)

Emerald Tree Boa

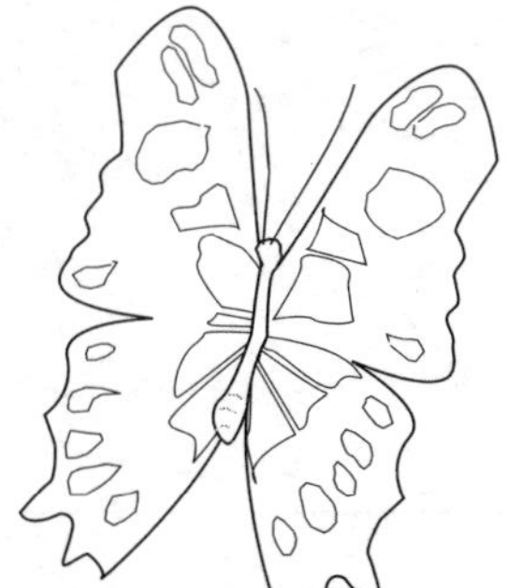

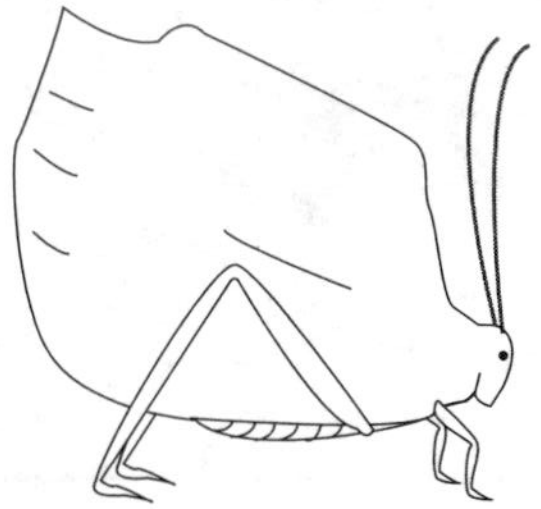

Katydid

Sloth

Tapir

Anteater

Iguana

Tree Porcupine

Butterfly

Laura Candler: *Wee Science*     **Kagan** Publishing • 1 (800) 933-2667 • www.KaganOnline.com

# Rain Forests of the Earth

## Color Key

1. Draw a dark **red** line over the *equator*.
2. Color the *tropical rain forests* **green**.
3. Color the rest of the *continents* **brown**.
4. Color the *oceans* **blue**.

# Simple Animal Sorting

Laura Candler: *Wee Science*          ***Kagan Publishing*** • 1 (800) 933-2667 • www.KaganOnline.com

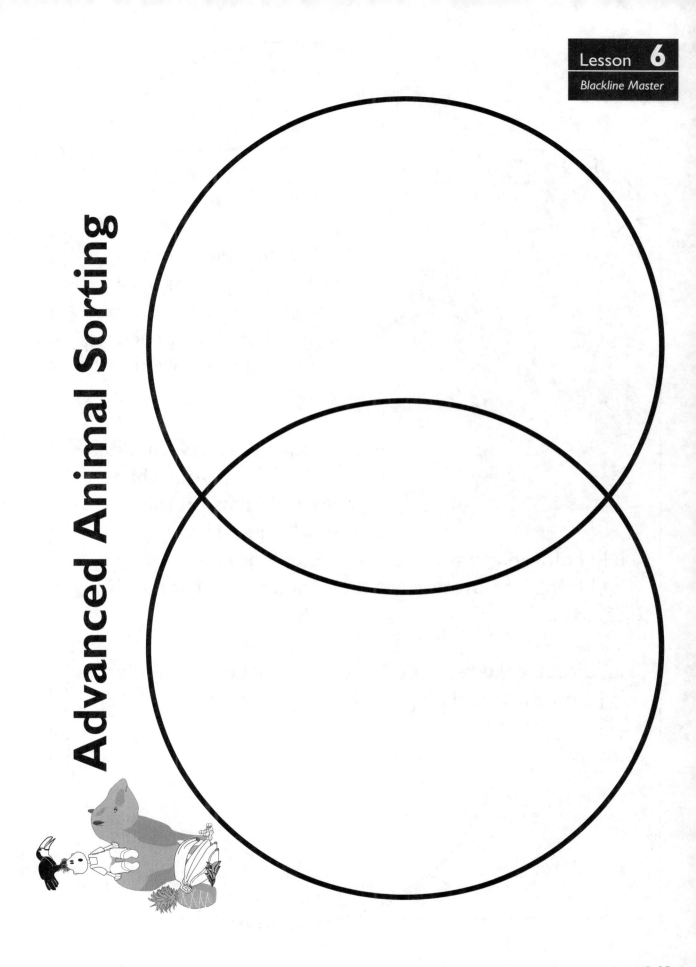

**Advanced Animal Sorting**

Dear Parents,

We have been studying tropical rain forests for the past few days. Did you know that many products we buy come from the rain forest?

Please take a few minutes to hunt with your child for the items on the worksheet. Have your child color in any products you find. If possible, let your child bring one or more of the products to share with the class.

Have your child return the worksheet and any rain forest items on the due date given below. Thank you!

Sincerely,


Due Date: _____

# From the Heart of the Rain Forest

| | | | |
|---|---|---|---|
| **Coconuts** | **Rubber** | **Coffee** | **Kiwi** |
| **Cinnamon** | **Bananas** | **Nutmeg** | **Chewing Gum** |
| **Wicker Furniture** | **Peanuts** | **Sugarcane** | **Cashews** |
| **Cocoa** | **Pineapple** | **Pepper** | **Brazil Nuts** |

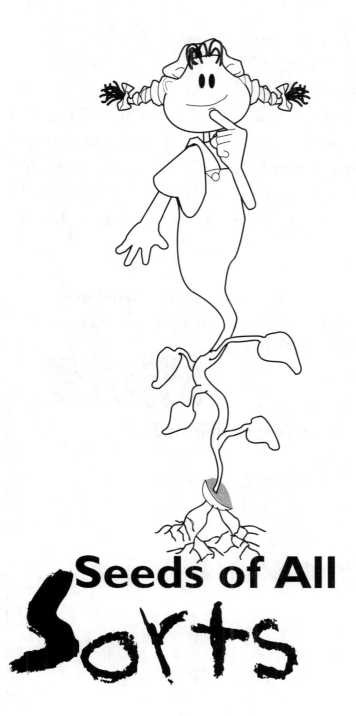

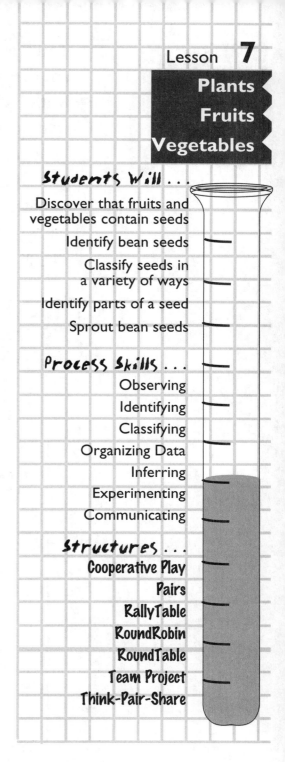

**Students Will...**

Discover that fruits and vegetables contain seeds

Identify bean seeds

Classify seeds in a variety of ways

Identify parts of a seed

Sprout bean seeds

**Process Skills...**

Observing

Identifying

Classifying

Organizing Data

Inferring

Experimenting

Communicating

**Structures...**

Cooperative Play

Pairs

RallyTable

RoundRobin

RoundTable

Team Project

Think-Pair-Share

# Seeds of All
# Sorts

eeds are one of the most simple and basic science topics to explore, yet the study of seeds never fails to fascinate children. This lesson provides numerous opportunities for students to investigate seeds while developing their classification skills. It's not necessary to complete every activity; be flexible in your planning and remain sensitive to your students' interest level. Don't rush the activities. Allow plenty of time for questions and free exploration.

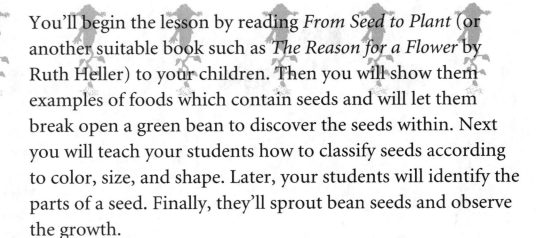

You'll begin the lesson by reading *From Seed to Plant* (or another suitable book such as *The Reason for a Flower* by Ruth Heller) to your children. Then you will show them examples of foods which contain seeds and will let them break open a green bean to discover the seeds within. Next you will teach your students how to classify seeds according to color, size, and shape. Later, your students will identify the parts of a seed. Finally, they'll sprout bean seeds and observe the growth.

Some parts of this lesson can be completed in a learning center. Note the circular "Learning Center" symbol next to these activities.

**1**

### *Reading about seeds using* TEACHER READS

**Materials for the Class:**
From *Seed to Plant* by Gail Gibbons (or any suitable book about seeds)

Read *From Seed to Plant* aloud to your students.

**2**

*Naming fruits and vegetables with seeds*
*using* **ROUNDROBIN**

Seat students in teams of four. Ask them to think of the fruits and vegetables they have eaten that have seeds in them. Then have them **RoundRobin** the names of those foods.

*Collect Fruits and Vegetables*
Obtain enough whole green beans (preferably raw) for each student to have one. Collect several examples of fruits and vegetables that have obvious seeds. Some examples are: apples, peaches, corn, Chinese pea pods, strawberries, lemons, and tomatoes.

**3**

*Showing seeds using* **TEACHER DEMONSTRATES**

**Materials for the Class:**
Several vegetables and fruits which contain seeds that are easy to observe

Show your students the fruit and vegetable examples you have brought to class. Pint out the seeds in each example. If the seeds are hidden, be sure to cut open the fruit or vegetable so that everyone can see the seeds within.

**4**

## *Discovering bean seeds using* INDIVIDUALS EXPLORE

**Materials for each Student:**
  1 whole raw green bean
  several dried beans

Give each child a whole raw green bean. Have them feel the bean and guess what is inside. Ask them to count the number of bumps they feel. Then show your students how to slip a fingernail between the halves of the pod and split it open. Let them take out the seeds and count them.

Then give each student several dried bean seeds. Caution them not to put the seeds in their mouths. Ask them to compare the two types of bean seeds. Tell them that the dried beans are seeds just like the ones that came out of the raw green bean. They have been dried out so that they could be stored easily.

Purchase a bag of 15-bean soup mix. If this is not available buy five or six types of dried beans and mix them in advance. Lentils, peas, kidney beans, lima beans, black beans, pinto beans, garbanzo beans and red beans would work well.

**5**

## *Exploring seeds using* COOPERATIVE PLAY

**Materials for each Student:**
  1 tablespoon dried beans – 15 bean soup variety
  1 small cup
  tray or paper plate

Give each person a tablespoon of fried beans in a small cup and a tray or plate. Have them pour their seeds onto the plate and allow time for unstructured play. Remind them not to put the seeds in their mouths at any time during the activity.

## Sorting beans using ROUNDTABLE

**Materials for each Student:**
15 bean soup mix
1 egg carton

Give each team an egg carton to use in sorting the seeds by type. Tell them to place the egg carton in the center of the team where everyone can see it. Have one person on each team begin by placing one of his or her seeds in the first section of the egg carton. The next person puts a different seed in the next compartment or the same type of seed in the first compartment. The students continue taking turns putting their seeds into the various sections so that all seeds are separated by type. Even though the soup mix has 15 types of beans, several are variations of the same species such as large, medium, and small lima beans. The 12 sections of the egg carton should provide plenty of space for separating the seeds.

### Preparing Lima Beans
At the conclusion of Activity 6, remove the large limas from the egg cartons and soak them overnight. Be sure you have at least one lima bean for each student. Pour the rest of the beans back into the soup mix bag and save them for the next sorting activity.

**7**

## Identifying bean seeds using THINK-PAIR-SHARE

**Materials for the Class:**
small cup of dried beans (15 bean soup variety)

**Materials for each Team:**
1 copy of the Types of Bean Seeds handout
1 egg carton of sorted bean seeds

For this activity, you will need to be familiar with the various types of beans in your soup mix. One way to learn the types of beans is to spend a few minutes in the grocery store examining the many types of dried beans available for cooking.

Give each team a copy of the Types of Bean Seeds handout. Hold up one dried bean from your cup and pronounce the name of that type of bean. Have students think about which of their beans would match that bean, then pair up with a partner and show each other an example of that bean from their egg carton Then cal on a student to share their choice with the class. Repeat with examples of all bean types.

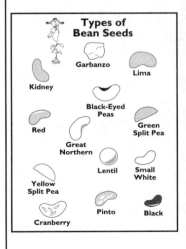

**Types of Bean Seeds**

Garbanzo

Lima

Kidney

Black-Eyed Peas

Red

Green Split Pea

Great Northern

Lentil

Small White

Yellow Split Pea

Cranberry

Pinto

Black

8

## Sorting by one attribute using PAIRS

**Materials for each Pair:**
1 tablespoon mixed dried beans
1 Simple Seed Sorting worksheet

### Step One: Discussing seeds
To begin the activity, give each pair a tablespoon of mixed dried beans. Tell your students that they are going to work together to sort the beans into several piles. They will need to look carefully at the beans and try to see how the beans are alike and different. First ask them to discuss with their partner the ways that some of the beans are alike. Then ask them to discuss the ways that the beans are different from each other.

### Step Two: Guided seed sorting
Now ask the students to place their beans in Circle A on the Simple Seed Sorting worksheet. Tell them that they are going to sort their beans into two piles so that all the beans in one pile are alike in some way. All the beans in the other pile must be different from those in the first pile.

Lead them through at least one example. In RallyTable fashion, have them take turns putting all the red seeds in Circle B and all the rest in Circle C. Say "These seeds are red, and these are 'not red'." Young children may need help with the concept "not" as in "not red." Children need to learn to describe their sets orally, using the word "not" rather than trying to describe all the different colors in the other pile.

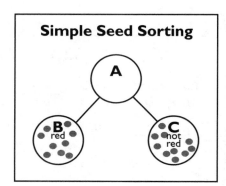

**Simple Seed Sorting**

A

B
red

C
not red

(continued on page 153)

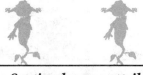

*Sorting by one attribute* (continued on page 152)
Write the word **attribute** on the board. Tell them that color is an "attribute" that can help us sort the beans into piles. All the beans have a color, even though they are not all the same color. Tell your students that the beans have many different attributes which can be used to sort them.

Guide your students through additional examples as needed, using such attributes as "round" and "not round," "speckled" and "not speckled," etc.

*Sorting Three: Independent seed sorting*
Now challenge your students to work with their partner to sort their beans by a different attribute. Have them place all their seeds back in Circle A and take turns moving them to Circle B or Circle C. Walk around and talk to each pair to find out how they are sorting their beans.

**9**

## *Using a branching classification system using* PAIRS

**Materials for each Pair:**
 2 tablespoons mixed dried beans
 1 Advanced Seed Sorting worksheet

### *Step One: Introducing the system*
Give each pair one copy of the Advanced Seed Sorting page. Tell them to put all their seeds into Circle A at the top of the page. Write the word **classify** on the board. Tell your students that to "classify" means to decide how things are alike and different so that you can put them into groups. Tell them that now they are ready to sort their beans into many different groups by thinking about the ways the beans are alike and different.

Lead the class through the entire sorting process the first time you introduce this classification system. Ask the pairs to put their heads together and discuss the ways the beans could be divided into just two piles. They should be able to draw upon their earlier experiences with Simple Seed Sorting. Let several students offer suggestions, and then pick a very easy attribute for the class to begin with. You might start with

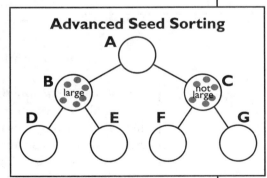

**Advanced Seed Sorting**

"large" and "not large" (small). You do not need to write the names of the categories on the page. If you feel words are needed, draw the illustration on the board and write the names of the attributes in the circles.

(continued on page 154)

### Using a branching classification system (continued from page 153)

#### Step Two: Sorting seeds
Use **RallyTable** for the actual sorting process. Ask one person in each pair to take a bean from the circle at the top and think about whether it is large or small. Allow the two to discuss that characteristic, and tell them that the words large and small aren't very exact. The two of them together will have to decide together where the bean goes. There are no specific right or wrong answers as long as the general guidelines are followed. Then have the other person choose another bean to classify. The two continue **RallyTable** sorting until all the beans in circle A have been moved to circles B and C.

#### Step Three: Discussing ways to sort seeds
Next, have the students look at just Circle B. Ask them to discuss ways they could divide just that set of beans into two more categories. Let several students share their ideas with the class. Choose one to do together and write the two attributes on the board. An example would be "speckled" and "not speckled."

#### Step Four: Sorting seeds
Have students use the same **RallyTable** structure used earlier to sort the beans in circle B. All beans from that circle should be moved into Circle D or E.

#### Step Five: Discussing ways to sort seeds
Now have students consider the beans left in circle C. Ask them to discuss ways that those beans could be divided into two piles. The classification scheme does not have to be the same as the one used to divide pile B. Choose one method for the class to use. Write the categories on the board.

**Advanced Seed Sorting**

A

B          C

D        E      F        G

speckled   not speckled   red   not red

#### Step Six: Sorting seeds
Have your students continue with the **RallyTable** method of sorting beans.

#### Step Seven: Discussing the classification of a particular bean
Now hold up a bean from one of the four categories. Ask the students to discuss why that bean is in that circle. They should name both attributes that were used to classify the bean. For example, "The bean is large and speckled." Continue with additional examples until everyone can explain why a particular bean was placed into a particular circle.

#### Step Eight: Creating classification systems
If your class has become comfortable with the classification process, have them put all the bean seeds in Circle A again. Then have each pair divide the beans according to their own sorting schemes. Let them challenge the pair across from them to figure out their classification system.

## Identifying seed parts using TEACHER TALK

**Materials for each Student:**
1 soaked lima bean

Give each student one soaked lima bean. Show them how to carefully open the bean by sliding a fingernail between he two halves. Have them examine the parts of the bean seed while you name them. Draw an illustration of a bean seed on the board, and have your students description of each bean part:

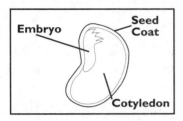

1. **embryo** - the baby plant
2. **seed coat** - the thin skin around the seed which protects it
3. **cotyledon** - the fleshy part of the seed which is the food for the baby plant

## Labeling an illustration using RALLYTABLE

**Materials for each Pair:**
1 copy of Parts of a Seed worksheet
2 pairs of scissors
1 bottle of glue

### Step One: Cutting out labels
Give each pair one copy of the Parts of a Seed worksheet, two pairs of scissors, and a bottle of glue. Have them cut off the section with the labels and work together to cut out the six individual labels.

### Step Two: Placing labels
Now have them divide the six labels randomly between themselves. Explain to them that for each bean part, there will be two labels. One names the part and the other describes the part. Show them how to take turns placing the labels in the correct locations on the worksheet. Leave your illustration on the board for them to use as a guide. Circulate around the room and check the placement of their labels before having them glue the labels in place.

**12**

## Sprouting bean seeds using TEAM PROJECT

**Materials for each Team:**
small cup of bean seeds (15 bean soup mix)
4 clear plastic cups
4 paper towels
water
clear tape
4 file folder labels
hand lens (optional)

### Step One: Explaining the experiment
Tell your students that they are now going to sprout some of the seeds they have been using in their activities. Each person on the team will choose a different type of seed to sprout.

### Step Two: Choosing seeds
Give each team four clear plastic cups and a small cup of mixed bean seeds. Have the first person choose one type of seed and take five of those seeds out of the cup. For instance, they may choose to sprout lentils and should take five lentils out of the cup. They then pass the cup to the next person who takes out five seeds of a different type. Continue until everyone has chosen their seeds. Discourage student from choosing the green or yellow split peas since these beans are not whole and won't sprout.

### Step Three: Labeling cups
Now give each person a file folder label and have them write their name on it. Tell them to stick the label to their clear plastic cup. Then have them take a small piece of clear tape and tape one of their seeds to the outside of the cup. After their seeds sprout, this will help them remember how their seed looked originally.

### Step Four: Soaking seeds
Have students put their remaining seeds in their cups and cover them with about an inch of water. Ask them to talk with their partner about what they think will happen to their seeds overnight.

(continued on page 157)

**Science Journal Suggestions**
**Vocabulary:** attribute, classify, embryo, cotyledon, seed coat
**Illustrations:** types of seeds, parts of seeds, seed sorting diagram,
pictures of bean seeds sprouting
**Writing:** describe the job of each seed part, name fruits and vegetables that
contain seeds, explain how to sort seeds

### Sprouting bean seeds (continued from page 156)

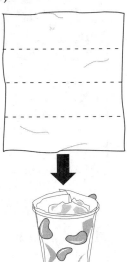

#### Step Five: Sprouting seeds

The next day, have your students pick their soaked seeds out of the cup. Give each person a paper towel and help them fold it the long way in fourths so that it will fit inside their cup. Show them how to slip the paper towel down inside the glass so that it sticks to the sides. Give them another paper towel to crumple up and stuff in the center. Have them slide their four bean seeds down between the paper towel and the cup. The beans need to be above the level of the water so they won't rot.

Place the cups in a warm location. They don't need to be in sunlight until they begin sprouting. If the paper towel dries out, add a small amount of water to keep it moist. Don't add too much water, however, or the seeds will begin to mildew and smell bad.

#### Step Six: Observing bean sprouts

Each day, let your students spend a few minutes observing and talking about their sprouting seeds. Have them pass the cups around the team so that they can see each other's seeds. Let them use hand lenses to make careful observations of the seeds' roots and the embryo as it emerges from the cotyledon. Encourage them to compare their seeds with seeds of other students on their team. Which one sprouted the fastest? Which one has the longest roots?

After a week or so, let your students take their sprouting seeds home. Drain the water first and remind them to add water when they get home. They may want to plant the sprouts in soil and watch them continue to grow.

#### For Younger Students

If the RallyTable "Parts of a Seed" activity is too difficult, modify it so that it becomes a word matching activity. Before the lesson, prepare one worksheet for each pair of students by gluing the names and jobs of each seed part in their proper places. Cut out a second set of word cards and have the students take turns placing the cards over the matching words on the worksheet.

You can also use the Types of Bean Seeds worksheet for a matching activity. Duplicate enough worksheets for each two students to have one between them. Use colored pencils to color the seed pictures as accurately as possible (look at actual seeds while you do this). Then give each pair of students a small cup of 15-bean soup mix and have them take turns placing each seed on the matching picture. Make sure you tell them that they may have pictures with no seeds to match, or they might have seeds left over that don't have a matching picture on the page. This is because different brands of soup mix contain different beans.

# Materials Check List

**For the Class:**
- ❑ *From Seed to Plant* by Gail Gibbons (or any suitable book about seeds)
- ❑ several vegetables and fruits which contain seeds that are easy to observe
- ❑ small cup of mixed dried beans – 15 bean soup variety

**For each Pair:**
- ❑ 1 Advanced Seed Sorting worksheet
- ❑ 1 Simple Seed Sorting worksheet
- ❑ 2 tablespoons mixed dried bean seeds
- ❑ 1 copy of Parts of a Seed worksheet
- ❑ 2 pairs of scissors
- ❑ 1 bottle of glue

**For each Team:**
- ❑ hand lens (optional)
- ❑ 1 egg carton
- ❑ water
- ❑ small cup of dried beans – 15 bean soup variety
- ❑ 1 copy of the Types of Bean Seeds handout
- ❑ 4 clear plastic cups
- ❑ 4 paper towels
- ❑ 4 file folder labels

**For each Student:**
- ❑ 1 whole raw green bean
- ❑ 1 tablespoon dried beans – 15 bean soup variety
- ❑ 1 small cup
- ❑ tray or paper plate
- ❑ 1 soaked lima bean

## Curriculum Links

**1. Math - Measuring lengths of seeds**
Have students line seeds up in order from shortest to longest. Then show them how to measure their seeds. Children who aren't ready for standard measurement can find out how many little seeds can be lined up to make a big seed.

**2. Math - Graphing a mixture of beans**
Let students sort one tablespoon of mixed beans into several piles by one attribute such as color. Have them count the number of each type of bean and glue the beans onto graph paper to form a bar graph.

**3. Literature - Reading fiction**
Read *A Tiny Seed* by Eric Carle to your class. Use **Think-Pair-Share** throughout the story to have students predict what will happen to the tiny seed.

**4. Creative Movement - Acting out a plant's life cycle**
Have students work together in small groups to form a seed, then a sprouting seed, and finally a seed that has grown into a plant.

**5. Science - Observing 15-Bean Soup**
Make 15-bean soup. Follow the directions on the package, but place the ingredients in a crock pot in your classroom (out of reach of students). Make sure to soak the beans overnight before making the soup. As the soup cooks, your students will be able to smell its aroma. Before they leave at the end of the day, give each one a small cup of soup to sample.

**6. Art - Making seed pictures**
Let students use seeds they have collected or seeds from the 15-bean soup mix to create pictures. Have them arrange the seeds in a pleasing pattern on a sheet of heavy construction paper, then let them glue the seeds in place.

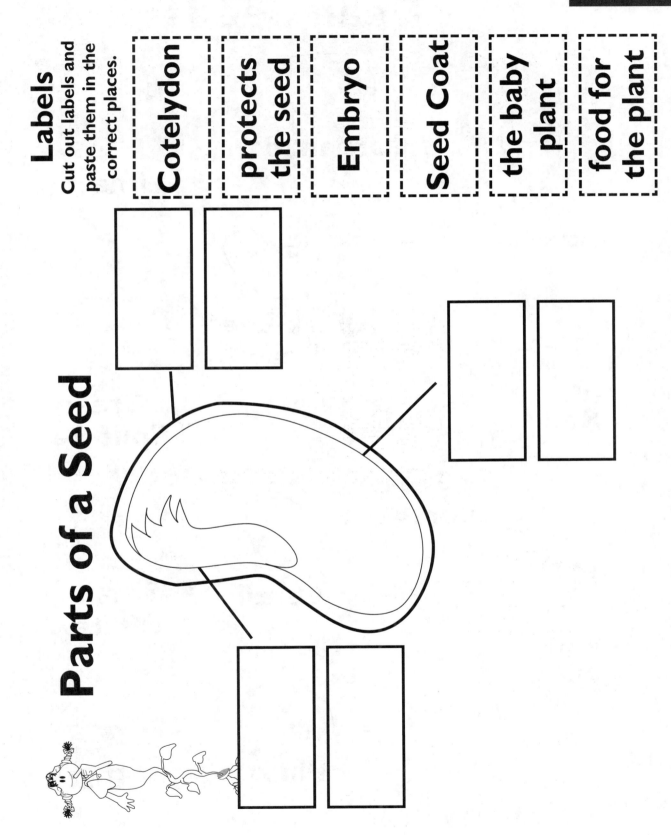

**Labels**
Cut out labels and paste them in the correct places.

Cotelydon

protects the seed

Embryo

Seed Coat

the baby plant

food for the plant

# Parts of a Seed

# Types of Bean Seeds

**Garbanzo**

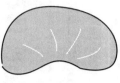

**Lima**

**Kidney**

**Black-Eyed Peas**

**Green Split Pea**

**Red**

**Great Northern**

**Lentil**

**Small White**

**Yellow Split Pea**

**Cranberry**

**Pinto**

**Black**

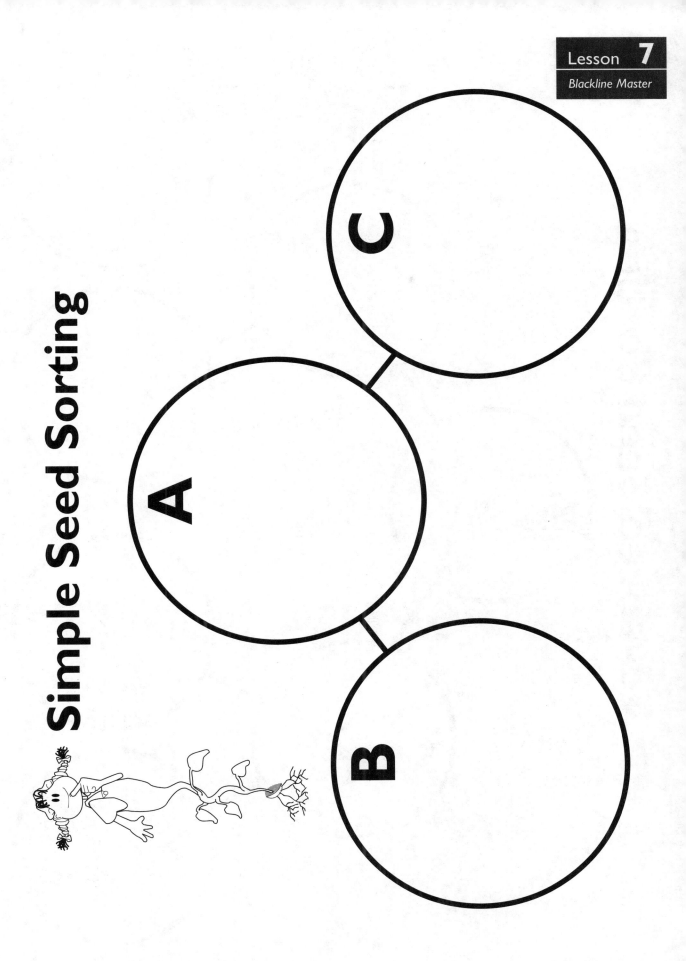

# Simple Seed Sorting

# Advanced Seed Sorting

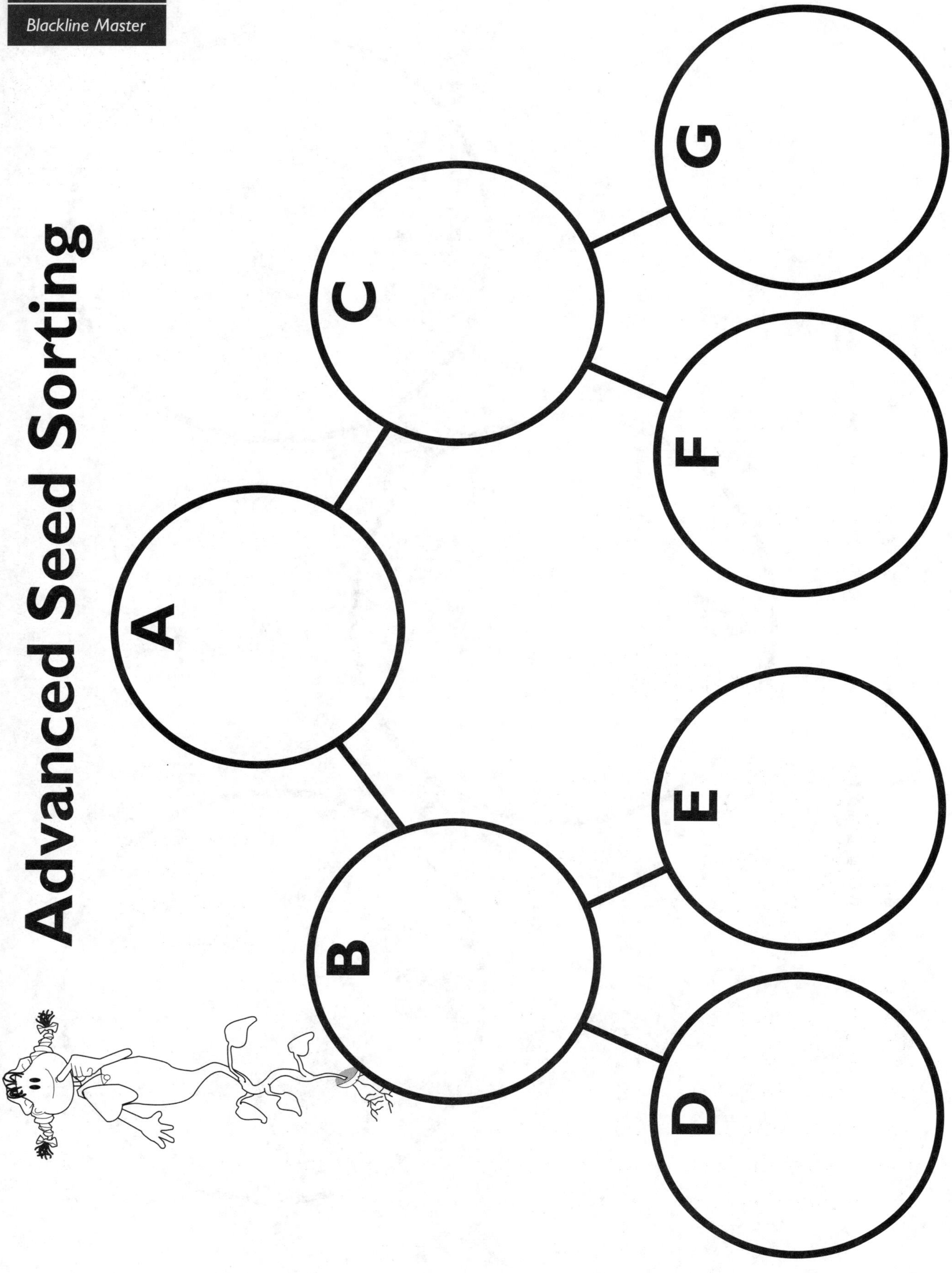

G

C

F

A

B

E

D

**Students Will . . .**

Listen to the story
*The Listening Walk*
by Paul Showers

Take a "Listening Walk"
and observe sounds

Make a Team Listening
Walk Picture Book

Identify sounds made by
common household objects

**Process Skills . . .**

Observing

Identifying

Inferring

Communicating

**Structures . . .**

Cooperative Play

Pairs

Team Interview

Team Project

Think-Pair-Share

Team RoundRobin

# Mystery Sounds

D istinguishing one sound from another is an important observational skill. Children need a variety of opportunities to fine-tune their sense of hearing. In this lesson, you will read *The Listening Walk* to your class. Then you'll lead your children on a listening walk to discover the sounds around them. After they return to the classroom they will draw pictures of some of the sounds they heard, compiling them to form Team Picture Books. You

will provide additional practice by creating sounds with common household objects (spoons, cans, rubber bands, etc.). Finally, each team will play a Mystery Sound game with a box of ordinary sound-making objects.

Some parts of this lesson can be completed by individual teams visiting a learning center. Note the circular "Learning Center" symbol next to activities that can be completed in this way.

**SAFETY**

Make sure students are carefully supervised on their Listening Walk. Avoid areas with heavy traffic. If you walk through the woods, watch out for poisonous plants and animals.

**SPOTLIGHT**

When using small objects for sound-makers, remind children not to put any of the objects in their mouths.

**1**

### Reading The Listening Walk
### *using* TEACHER READS

**Materials for the Class:**
*The Listening Walk* by Paul Showers

Read *The Listening Walk* to your students. This story is about a girl who goes for a walk with her father. Instead of talking, they listen to all the sounds in the neighborhood.

**2**

### *Taking the Listening Walk using* PAIRS

Ask your children if they would like to go on a listening walk too. Within their teams of four, divide them into pairs. The partners walk side-by-side without talking, just listening. Guide the class through the school yard to a place where they can all sit down.

Have your students form a large Listening Circle, with everyone next to their partner. Ask them to close their eyes and listen to all the different sounds they can hear. After one minute, have them turn to their partner and discuss those sounds.

Next, tell your children that when they return to class they will draw pictures of two of the sounds they heard. Tell them to look closely at the objects (or people) making the sounds so that they will know what to draw. When everyone is ready, walk them back to the classroom.

**3**

### *Making Picture Books using* TEAM PROJECT

**Materials for each Student:**
  I Listening Walk Picture Book worksheet

**Materials for each Team:**
  I box of crayons
  I sheet of construction paper (9 x 12)

Seat your students in teams of four. Give each student one copy of the Listening Walk Picture Book worksheet. Have them draw two different sounds they heard on their listening walk. If your students can write, have them label each picture with the name of the object and the sound it makes (i.e. airplane, vvrroomm).

Help your students to cut apart the two pictures on the dotted line. Assemble all eight pictures to form a booklet. Then fold the construction paper in half the short way and slip the pictures inside. Staple in several places along the inside edge to hold the booklet together. Write "Our Listening Walk" on the cover and let everyone on the team help decorate it.

**4**

### *Sharing Picture Books using* TEAM ROUNDROBIN

Provide some time for each team to share their Listening Walk Book with the class. Seat the entire class in a large circle, allowing team members to sit with each other. Call on one student from each team to serve as a Reporter who will show their team's Listening Walk Picture Book to the rest of the class. When the activity is over, display the booklets in a prominent place.

### *Collect Sound Makers*

Several days before Activity 5 ask your students to bring in several objects which make interesting sounds when shaken, tapped, or rolled. Show them some examples, such as dried beans inside a plastic container, beads, marbles, rubberbands, spoons, toothbrushes, spools of thread and keys.

**5**

### *Exploring sound makers using* COOPERATIVE PLAY

**Materials for each Team:**
sound-making objects brought by students

Have the students take out all the sound-making objects they brought from home. Give them plenty of time to play with the objects in an unstructured manner. Just ask, "What sounds can you make with your objects?" Then let them explore. Encourage them to tell their teammates what they discover.

**6**

## Identifying Mystery Sounds using THINK-PAIR-SHARE

**Materials for the Class:**
  an assortment of sound-making objects
  a large box to hold objects

Place an assortment of sound-making objects in a large box. Show the objects to the class and tell them that you will be using the objects to make Mystery Sounds. They will have to listen very carefully and think of what objects in the box might be making the sound. Say that you might shake, tap, or even roll the objects. Turn the box on its side so that you can see the contents, but so that your children can not see the objects.

Start with a simple sound, such as keys jangling. As you create the sound, ask your children to close their eyes and think of the object that might make that sound. Tell them to open their eyes and give a thumbs-up signal when they think they know.

Next, have them pair with their partner and discuss their guess. Finally, call on several students randomly to share what they thought the sound was. Show the class the object as you make the sound one more time.

Continue using **Think-Pair-Share** to have children identify sounds. When children are able to guess a single sound easily, combine two objects to form a new sound. Roll a marble around the inside of a plastic cup, for instance, and have the children think about which two objects are making the sound.

**7**

## *Making Mystery Sounds using* TEAM INTERVIEW

**Materials for each Team:**
an assortment of sound-making objects
1 large box

### Step One: Explaining the activity
Tell your children that now they will get to make Mystery Sounds for their teammates to guess. Explain that they will take turns being Mystery Sound Makers. Tell them that when they are they the Mystery Sound Maker they will choose one or two objects from the box to use in making a sound. Everyone on the team will have to guess the sound. Then someone else will have a turn as the Sound Maker.

Give each team a cardboard box. Have them place all the sound-making objects they brought to school in the box.

### Step Two: Numbering off
Number the students on each team from 1 to 4. Make sure each student knows his or her number (pin numbered tags on each child if necessary).

(continued on page 169)

**7 cont.**

*Making Mystery Sounds* (continued from page 168)

*Step Three: Making the first sound*
Tell Person #1 on each team that they will be the first Mystery Sound Maker. Have them take the team's box of materials and turn it on its side so the others can't see inside. Tell the Mystery Sound Makers to choose one or two objects and use them to make a sound.

*Step Four: Guessing the sound*
Tell everyone else to close their eyes and try to picture the object that is making that sound. When they think they know it, they open their eyes and give a thumbs-up signal. When everyone on the team has their eyes open and a thumb up, they discuss their guess. If they don't agree, they can ask to hear it again. When they all agree, they tell their guess to the Sound Maker. If they are wrong, the Sound Maker makes the sound again and gives them another chance. If the team still can't guess it, the Mystery Sound Maker shows the team how the sound is being made.

*Step Five: Rotating roles*
After one round of the Mystery Sound activity, Person #2 becomes the Mystery Sound Maker. Continue until all team members have had a chance to be the Sound Maker or until the class period is over.

*Science Journal Suggestions*
Vocabulary: sounds, items heard on Listening Walk
Illustrations: pictures of things heard on Listening Walk
Writing: describing sounds, telling about the Listening Walk

# Materials
# Check
# List

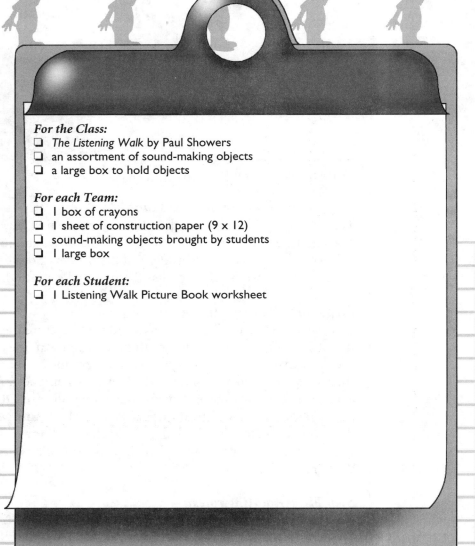

**For the Class:**
❏ *The Listening Walk* by Paul Showers
❏ an assortment of sound-making objects
❏ a large box to hold objects

**For each Team:**
❏ 1 box of crayons
❏ 1 sheet of construction paper (9 x 12)
❏ sound-making objects brought by students
❏ 1 large box

**For each Student:**
❏ 1 Listening Walk Picture Book worksheet

## Curriculum Links

### 1. Music - Creating musical instruments
Have students combine some of the objects they brought from home to create musical instruments. Stretch rubber bands around open cans, put beans inside of boxes, make clackers out of spoons, etc. Let each team make up their own music to play for the class.

### 2. Language Arts - Writing about sounds
Have a parent volunteer or teacher's assistant take each team of students and a tape recorder on a "sound hunt." Have the students identify and record sounds that they hear. When each team has had a chance to contribute to the tape, play the tape for the class and ask students to write the sounds they hear. Very young children can use "inventive" spelling or draw pictures of the sounds.

### 3. Math - Recognizing patterns
Young children learn about patterns by listening and extending sound patterns. Establish a clapping or stomping pattern and have students continue the pattern you have begun. Then let individual students make up their own patterns for their teammates to follow.

### 4. Science - Matching sound patterns
Prepare a set of film canisters with pairs of matching sound-making objects. For example, fill two cans with rice, two cans with cotton, two cans with paper clips, etc. Place these in a learning center and allow students to discover which cans have sounds that match.

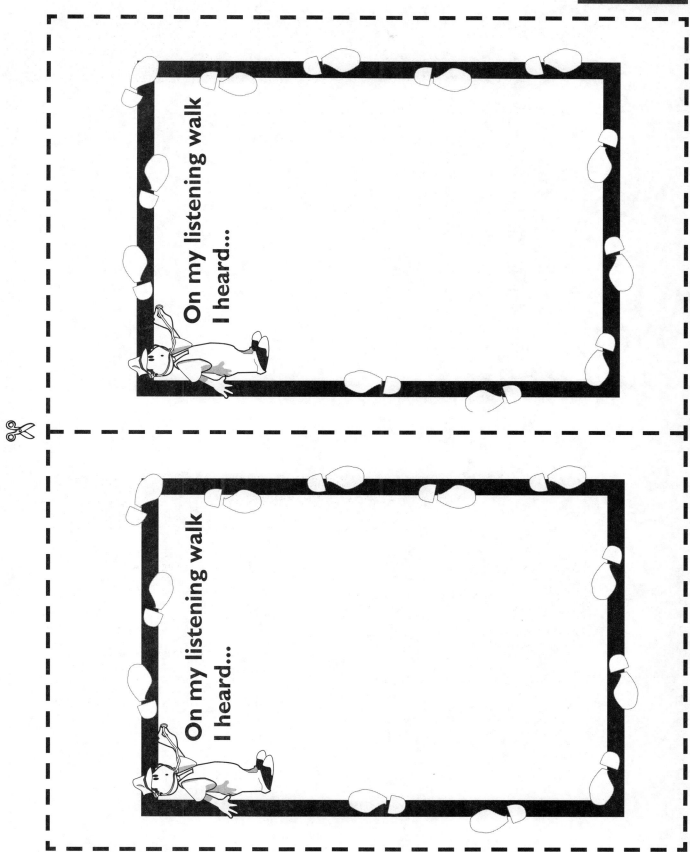

On my listening walk
I heard...

On my listening walk
I heard...

*Students Will...*

Draw a goldfish before
and after observing one

Listen to a book about fish

Learn the parts of a fish

Assemble paper fish
parts into a complete fish

Create a Team Ocean
Habitat Poster

*Process Skills...*

Observing

Identifying

Making Models

Inferring

Communicating

*Structures...*

Numbered Heads Together

RallyTable

Team Discussion

Team Project

Think-Pair-Share

## Something's Fishy

**C**lassroom pets can make wonderful subjects for science instruction. In this lesson, your children will draw a fish before actually observing one. Then they will carefully observe a live goldfish and will sketch a second, more accurate fish picture. They'll listen to *Fish Fish Fish* and discuss the parts of a fish. After reviewing the parts with **Numbered Heads Together,** they will work in pairs to label a fish diagram. Next, they will cut out and assemble paper fish parts. Finally, they will create Team Posters with their paper fish.

**1**

## *Drawing a fish using* **INDIVIDUALS DRAW**

**Materials for each Student:**
1 Fishy Observations worksheet

**Materials for each Team:**
1 goldfish in a small transparent container

Ask if anyone has ever seen a goldfish. Give each student a copy of the Fishy Observations worksheet and ask them to fold it in half so that only the top fishbowl is showing. Ask your children to draw a goldfish in the fish bowl. Do not give any help or clues at this point; just tell them to draw what they think a goldfish looks like.

### *Obtain Goldfish*

You will need one goldfish (or other small fish) for each team of 4 - 5 students. If you only have one fish for the whole class, this first part of the lesson can be completed in a learning center. You may want to set up a class aquarium, but don't let the students observe the fish prior to the lesson. Instructions for preparing an aquarium and caring for fish are not included in this lesson; many excellent books are available on this subject. If you don't want to purchase an aquarium, you may be able to borrow one from a friend or a pet store.

SAFETY

SPOTLIGHT

Place the goldfish into unbreakable transparent containers for the observation part of the lesson. Make sure the containers are resting on flat surfaces.

**2**

## *Observing a live fish using* **TEAM DISCUSSION**

Place a small container with a goldfish in the center of each team. If you only have one goldfish for the class, place the container in a learning center and allow each team time for observation. Tell them to talk about all the parts of the goldfish that they see. Ask them to count the number of fins and discuss how the fish uses each body part.

## 3

### Drawing a live goldfish
### *using* INDIVIDUALS DRAW

Now tell everyone to open their worksheet and draw another goldfish in the bottom fishbowl. This time they should try to draw the fish as it really looks. Make sure they are looking at the goldfish while they are drawing.

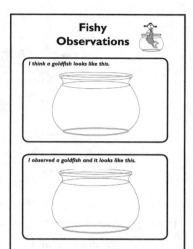

**Fishy Observations**

*I think a goldfish looks like this.*

*I observed a goldfish and it looks like this.*

## 4

### *Reading about fish using* TEACHER READS

**Materials for the Class:**
*Fish Fish Fish* by Georgie Adams (or other suitable fish book)

Read *Fish Fish Fish* to your students. Before you read, ask them to listen to find out more about the parts of a fish. If this book is not available, substitute a different fish book that clearly shows the parts of a fish.

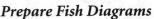

### Prepare Fish Diagrams

Prepare two posters or transparencies of the Fish Diagram. Label the parts on one and make one without any labels.

**5**

## Discussing fish parts using THINK-PAIR-SHARE

**Materials for the Class:**
poster or transparency of labeled and unlabeled Fish Diagram

**Materials for each Team:**
1 set of Fish Part cards

### Step One: Naming parts

Now have your students sit with a partner and discuss the questions below. Call out each question separately and have students think about their own answer, then pair with their partner to discuss it. Finally, ask students to share their ideas with the class.

**What are some parts of a fish?**
**How are some parts of a fish like our body parts?**

### Step Two: Discussing each part

Now show the poster or overhead transparency of the labelled fish. Give each team a set of Fish Parts cards. Have them spread the cards out so that all members can see and touch them. Point to the various fish parts and have all children touch the card with that part's name. Talk about the letters and sounds in the name, and have the class practice saying the name by repeating it in unison.

Tell the children that each part of the fish has a special job. Use **Think-Pair-Share** to discuss each body part. First have students think about what the part is used for, then pair with a partner to talk about it. Finally, have students share their ideas with the class.

(continued on page 177)

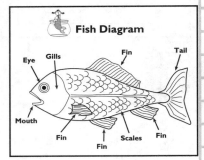

**Fish Diagram**

Eye  Gills  Fin  Tail
Mouth  Fin  Fin  Scales  Fin

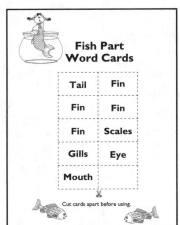

**Fish Part
Word Cards**

| Tail | Fin |
|------|-----|
| Fin | Fin |
| Fin | Scales |
| Gills | Eye |
| Mouth | |

Cut cards apart before using.

*Discussing fish parts* (continued from page 176)

Discuss the following functions of each fish part:

**Scales** The scales are the "skin" of the fish which protects its body.

**Fins** Fins are used for moving the fish through the water and help it stay balanced. Fins do a job similar to our arms and legs.

**Gills** Gills allow the fish to breathe while swimming. (Water is drawn through the mouth and across the gills. The gills take the air out of the water.) Gills do the same job as a person's lungs.

**Mouth** A fish's mouth is used for feeding as well as drawing water in and across the gills.

**Eyes** The eyes are located on either side of the head and allow the fish to see to the right and the left at the same time. Fish eyes have no eyelids. Eyelids on animals held keep the eye moist and are not needed underwater.

*Prepare Fish Part Cards*

Make a set of Fish Parts cards for each team. To do so, duplicate the Fish Parts Word Cards, cut them apart, and glue each word on an index card. Or simply write the names of the fish parts on index cards.

You'll need one card for each of the following words: mouth, gills, scales, fin, tail, and eye.

**6**

*Reviewing the parts of a fish*
*using* NUMBERED HEADS TOGETHER

**Materials for the Class:**
1 unlabeled Fish Diagram

**Materials for each Team:**
1 set of Fish Part cards

*Step One: Numbering off*
Seat students in teams of four. Assign each person a number from 1 to 4 or one of four different colors.

*Step Two: Posing a question*
Make sure each team has a set of Fish Part cards. Show the poster of the unlabelled fish. Point to one part and ask, "What is the name of this part and how does it help the fish?" Ask everyone to think of their answer. Let them look at the Fish Part cards while they are trying to think of their answer.

(continued on page 178)

## 6 cont.

### Reviewing the parts of a fish (continued from page 177)

**Step Three: Discussing the answer**
Tell team members to lean forward and put their heads together to discuss the answer to the question. They should make sure everyone on the team knows the name of the body part and its job.

**Step Four: Calling a number**
Call a number from 1 to 4 (or name one of the four colors). That person on each team should find the card with the correct fish part name. On a count of three, have those students hold up the card. Call on one person to tell how that body part helps the fish. As a class, discuss the correct answer.

**Step Five: Repeating with new questions**
Point to a new fish part and follow steps one through four above.

## 7

### Labelling a fish diagram using RALLYTABLE

**Materials for each Pair:**
1 copy Fish Part Word Cards
2 pairs of scissors
1 Parts of a Fish worksheet

**Step One: Preparing word cards**
Give each pair of students one set of Fish Part Word Cards and scissors. Have one person cut down the center and give half to the other person. Tell both students to cut apart their word cards. Then give them one Parts of a Fish worksheet to share.

**Step Two: Labelling the fish**
Now have one person begin by placing one of his or her word cards in the correct place on the diagram. Have that person name the body part and talk about that part's job. For instance, as the word "mouth" is placed on the diagram the student says "This is the mouth and the fish uses it for eating."

Next, have the other student place one word card and discuss its job. The students take turns placing word cards until the worksheet is completed.

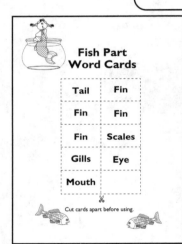

**Fish Part Word Cards**

| Tail | Fin |
|------|-----|
| Fin | Fin |
| Fin | Scales |
| Gills | Eye |
| Mouth | |

Cut cards apart before using.

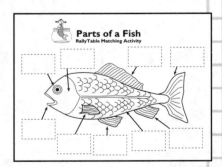

**Parts of a Fish**
RallyTable Matching Activity

**8**

## Creating Posters using TEAM PROJECT

**Materials for each Student:**
1 Make A Fish worksheet

**Materials for each Team:**
white butcher paper
box of 8 crayons
glue
pictures of ocean habitat

Make A Fish

In this activity, each person on the team will assemble and color one complete fish from cut-outs. Then the team will create a poster of an ocean habitat and will glue their fish onto the poster.

### Step One:  Assembling fish parts

Give each student a Make A Fish worksheet and have them cut out the parts. Let students work in pairs to assemble the parts into complete fish. Show them how to put a dot of glue on the tabs and glue the tab behind the fish's body. Leave up the poster or transparency of the labelled fish so that they will know where to place all the parts. Have students color their fish after they glue it together.

### Step Two:  Drawing an ocean habitat

Give each team a large sheet of white butcher paper and the eight crayon colors listed below. Show them pictures in magazines or books of an ocean habitat. Tell them that an animal's habitat is the place where it lives. Point out features that are often a part of the ocean, such as seaweed, rocks, shells, and sand.

Assign the following two colors to each person:

        **#1 - blue and red**        **#2 - green and yellow**
        **#3 - brown and pink**       **#4 - black and orange**

Each child may use only the colors given to him or her, and all colors must appear on the finished poster. Tell them to leave a large blue area open where they will glue the fish they assembled earlier.

(continued on page 180)

## 8 cont.

### Creating Posters (continued from page 179)

**Step Three: Adding fish to the poster**
Finally, let each person place his or her completed fish on the poster. Make sure all the fish fit before gluing any down. The fish may overlap the ocean features or each other. When everyone has agreed upon the placement of the fish, let them take turns gluing down their own fish.

Display the posters in a prominent location.

### Science Journal Suggestions
**Vocabulary:** mouth, eye, gills, scales, fin, habitat
**Illustrations:** fish, ocean habitat
**Writing:** how each body part helps the fish survive, describe a fish's habitat

### For Younger Students
Kindergarten teachers can make the **RallyTable** activity easier by turning it into a word matching activity. Prepare a gameboard for each pair of students by gluing one set of word cards in the proper places on the **RallyTable** worksheet. Then have students take turns placing their word cards on top of the matching word on the gameboard.

### For Older Students
Older children may enjoy learning more advanced terms for the fish body parts (see illustration). The fins have specific names: dorsal, pelvic, anal, and pectoral. Fish also have a lateral line which is a line of tiny holes (special pores) that help a fish sense vibrations in the water. The lateral line gives the sense of touch to a fish, so it could be compared to human fingertips.

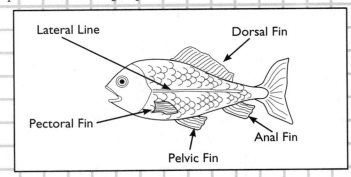

# Materials Check List

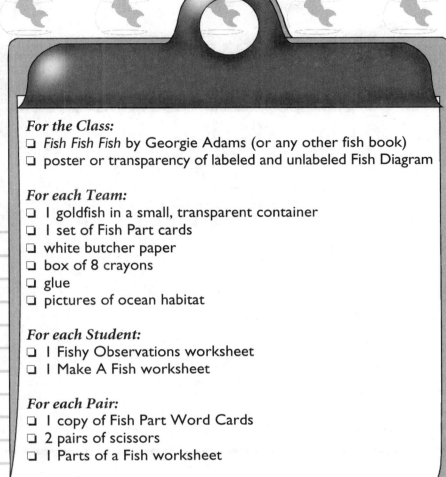

*For the Class:*
- ❏ *Fish Fish Fish* by Georgie Adams (or any other fish book)
- ❏ poster or transparency of labeled and unlabeled Fish Diagram

*For each Team:*
- ❏ 1 goldfish in a small, transparent container
- ❏ 1 set of Fish Part cards
- ❏ white butcher paper
- ❏ box of 8 crayons
- ❏ glue
- ❏ pictures of ocean habitat

*For each Student:*
- ❏ 1 Fishy Observations worksheet
- ❏ 1 Make A Fish worksheet

*For each Pair:*
- ❏ 1 copy of Fish Part Word Cards
- ❏ 2 pairs of scissors
- ❏ 1 Parts of a Fish worksheet

## Curriculum Links

**1. Literature - Reading fish fiction**
Read *The Rainbow Fish* by Marcus Pfister to your class. It's a wonderful story of a fish who finds happiness by learning to share.

**2. Writing - Writing about fish**
Have students imagine that they are a fish and write a short story about their adventures.

**3. Art - Making clay fish**
Give each team member one color of modeling clay. Have them work together to create a clay fish model using all the colors.

**4. Math - Measuring the paper fish**
Before students glue their paper fish onto their posters, let them measure their fish in either standard or nonstandard units.

**5. Creative Movement - Pretending to be fish**
Play soft music and have children pretend to be fish moving through the water. Give them different scenarios to act out such as eating smaller fish or escaping from a shark.

**6. Science - Taking a field trip**
Take your class to visit an aquarium. Have them draw some of the fish they see in their Science Journals.

# Fishy Observations

**I think a goldfish looks like this.**

**I observed a goldfish and it looks like this.**

Laura Candler: *Wee Science*      ***Kagan Publishing*** • 1 (800) 933-2667 • www.KaganOnline.com

# Fish Diagram

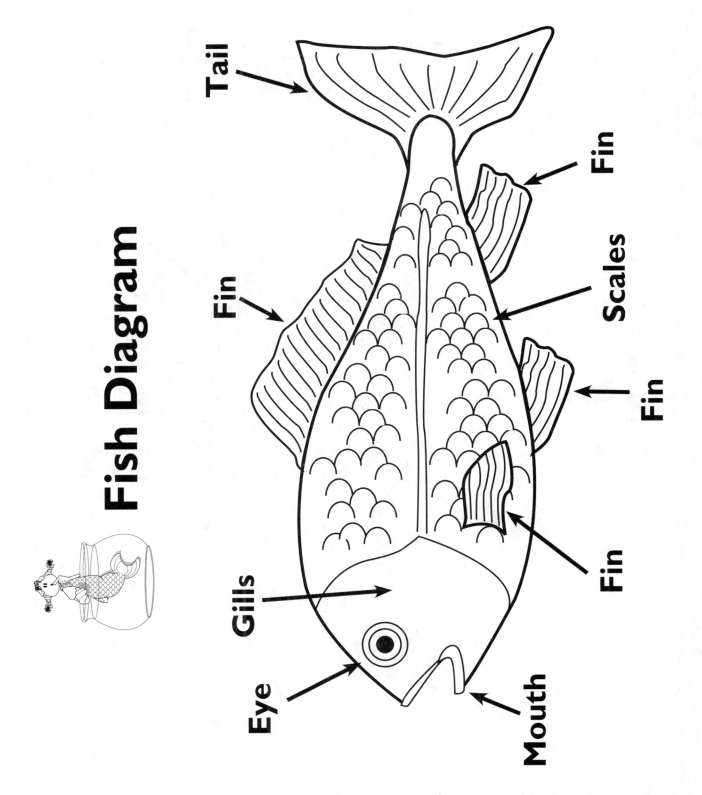

Tail

Fin

Scales

Fin

Fin

Gills

Eye

Mouth

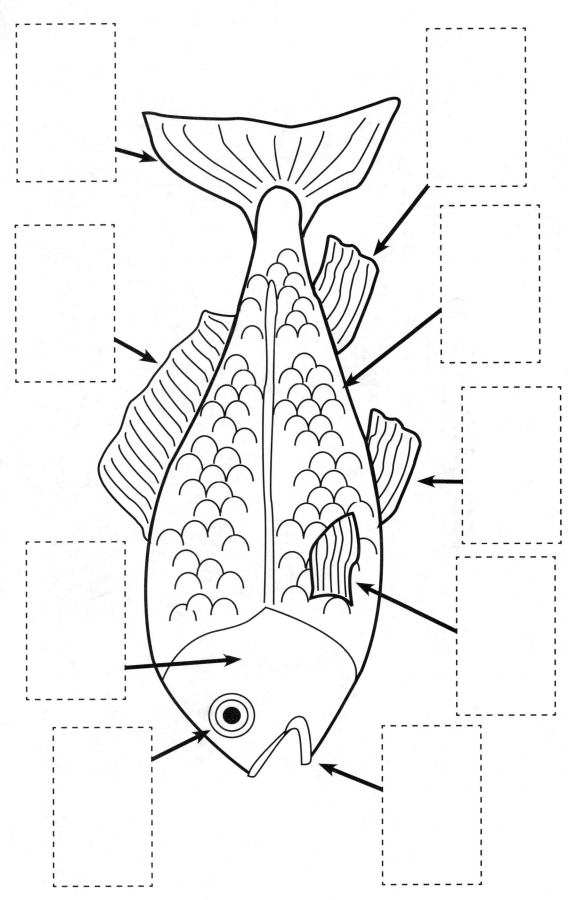

# Parts of a Fish
## RallyTable Matching Activity

Laura Candler: *Wee Science*          ***Kagan* Publishing** • 1 (800) 933-2667 • www.KaganOnline.com

# Fish Part
# Word Cards

| | |
|---|---|
| **Tail** | **Fin** |
| **Fin** | **Fin** |
| **Fin** | **Scales** |
| **Gills** | **Eye** |
| **Mouth** | |

Cut cards apart before using.

# Make A Fish

### Students Will...

Name and discuss
things that fly

Observe paper dropping and
infer reasons why it "floats"

Play with paper helicopters

Experiment with
paper helicopters

### Process Skills...

Observing

Predicting

Making Models

Organizing Data

Inferring

Experimenting

Communicating

### Structures...

Cooperative Play

Corners

Pairs

RallyTable

RoundRobin

Think-Pair-Share

Think-Pair-Square

# Helicopter Capers

**P** laying with homemade helicopters is an excellent way for students to learn that air helps make things fly. In this lesson, your students will name and discuss things that fly. Then they'll observe a crumpled piece of paper and a flat piece of paper falling and will try to figure out why the crumpled paper falls faster. Working with a partner they'll make and play with paper helicopters. Finally, they'll conduct an experiment to find out which paper helicopter stays in the air longer.

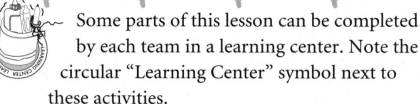

Some parts of this lesson can be completed by each team in a learning center. Note the circular "Learning Center" symbol next to these activities.

**1**

### *Naming things that fly using* ROUNDROBIN

Tell your students that they will be learning about air and how it can help things fly. Ask them to take turns naming things that fly. Designate one person on each team (by number or color) to begin. Have the members **RoundRobin** things that fly until they run out of ideas.

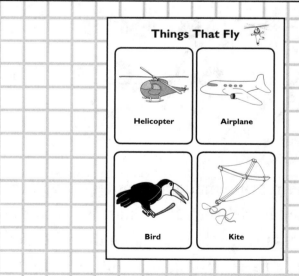

Things That Fly

| | |
|---|---|
| Helicopter | Airplane |
| Bird | Kite |

Laura Candler: *Wee Science*     *Kagan Publishing* • 1 (800) 933-2667 • www.KaganOnline.com

***Making Posters***
Make four posters (one for each corner of the room). Enlarge the pictures and words found on the "Things That Fly" page, drawing each picture on a separate sheet of 12 x 18 construction paper. Under each picture, write the name of the object in block letters.

**2**

## *Stating preferences using* CORNERS

**Materials for the Class:**
4 prepared posters of Things That Fly
tape
toy helicopter (optional)
toy airplane (optional)

**Materials for each Student:**
scrap paper
pencil or crayon

### *Step One: Discussing things that fly*
Show your students the four posters you prepared earlier of a bird, a kite, an airplane and a helicopter. Ask them to tell you ways those things are alike and different. When you discuss the helicopter and airplane, make sure your students understand the differences in how an airplane and a helicopter take off and land. If possible, use a toy helicopter to show how the blades spin around and lift the helicopter straight up. Show them how the airplane has to move forward faster and faster until it can build up enough speed to lift off the ground.

After you discuss the four items, tape one poster in each corner of the room.

### *Step Two: Stating preferences*
Now ask your students to imagine that they could be an airplane, a helicopter, a bird, or a kite. Which one would they be? Give each student a piece of scrap paper. Have them write down the word or the first letter of the object they would like to become.

(continued on page 190)

## 2 cont.

*Stating preferences* (continued from page 189)

### Step Three: Moving to corners
Now tell them to go to the corner which shows the object they would like to be. Have them bring their scrap paper to compare their word with the word on the poster.

### Step Four: Finding partners
Tell your students to pair up with one other person in their corner. They should link arms with that person so you can tell who are partners. Make sure everyone has a partner before continuing.

### Step Five: Discussing reasons
Finally, ask your students to tell their partner why they picked bird, kite, airplane, or helicopter. After they have a chance to discuss their reasons, have them return to their seats.

## 3

*Observing air's effect on paper*
*using* THINK-PAIR-SHARE

**Materials for the Class:**
 2 sheets of bond paper in different colors

### Step One: Introducing the experiment
Make sure everyone has a partner. Show the class two different colored sheets of paper. The sheets should be identical except for the color.

Write the word **experiment** on the board and tell the class they are going to help you do some experiments with the paper. Tell them that an experiment is when you do something to find out what happens.

### Step Two: Making predictions
Hold the sheets about 4 feet high and ask your students to think about which sheet of paper will land first if you drop them at the same time. Tell them that they are making a prediction. Then have them pair with their partner and discuss their predictions. Finally, let a few students share their ideas with the class. Write the word **prediction** on the board and jot down one or two predictions.

(continued on page 191)

**Observing air's effect on paper** (continued from page 190)

**Step Three: Testing predictions**
Now drop the sheets of paper at the same time. Both should land on the floor at approximately the same time. Pick the sheets up and drop them again to show that the same thing happens again. Ask someone to tell you what happened. Write the word **result** on the board and tell them that "result" means what happened. Next to the word "result" write "Both papers landed at the same time."

**Step 3**          **Step 4**

**Step Four: Making predictions**
Now crumple one of the sheets of paper tightly into a ball. Ask the students to think about which sheet of paper would land first. Then have them pair and discuss their ideas. Finally, let some students share their ideas with the class. Point out that they are making another prediction. Write some of their predictions on the board.

**Step Five: Testing predictions**
Now drop both papers from the same height. Do this several times. The crumpled paper will fall much faster. Ask students to think about what the result of the experiment was, then pair with a partner to discuss it. Finally, ask them to share their ideas with the class. Write "The crumpled paper landed first."

**4**

**Discussing results using THINK-PAIR-SQUARE**

Ask students to think about why the crumpled paper fell faster. Have them pair with their partner and to talk about their ideas. Next, have them square their ideas with their team. Then let a few students share with the class. Make sure they understand that gravity makes things fall to the ground but the air all around us pushes up on falling objects. The open sheet of paper has more space for the air to push back up. Both sheets of paper still weigh the same, which can be proven with a simple scale. If they think the color of the paper was important, smooth out the crumpled sheet and crumple up the flat sheet. Do the experiment again to show them that the color was not important. Different colors were used so that the students could tell one sheet of paper from the other.

**5**

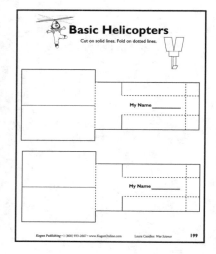

## Making helicopters using PAIRS

### Materials for each Pair:
  1 copy of Basic Helicopters
  scissors

Tell your students that they are going to learn more about things that fly by making toy helicopters. Tell them that the toys are called helicopters because they have wings that spin around like a real helicopter.

Give each pair of students one copy of the Basic Helicopters page. Let them work together but have them each make a helicopter. Model the steps for them by making your own helicopter and having them make theirs along with you. Use the illustration as a guide.

1. **Cut out the helicopter by carefully cutting around it on the solid lines.**
2. **Make three cuts into the helicopter on the solid lines.**
3. **Write your name on the base of the helicopter.**
4. **Form the base of the helicopter by folding the sides away from your name and the bottom up.**
5. **Fold one wing one direction and the other wing the other direction.**
6. **Decorate the helicopter by coloring it with interesting designs.**

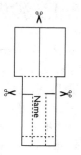 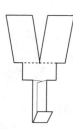 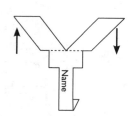

**6**

*Exploring helicopters*
*using* **COOPERATIVE PLAY**

**Materials for each Team:**
crayons
small bowl
paper clips
scissors
**Materials for each Person:**
1 Basic Helicopter

Now show your students how to launch their helicopters by standing on a chair and dropping them. Caution them to be careful not to fall while launching their helicopters.

Ask them "What can you find out about your helicopter?" Then let them work with their partner to discover everything they can about their helicopters. Walk around the room and let each pair share something with you that they have discovered. Encourage your students to experiment with their helicopters by changing them in some way. Have them try folding the wings the opposite direction, folding both the same way, cutting the wings, or adding a paperclip to the bottom. Ask them to place a bowl on the floor to make a target and to try to drop the helicopter into the bowl. Suggest helicopter races. Express interest in every innovative idea they come up with, and don't worry if they completely destroy their helicopters in the process of exploring them. Provide extra helicopter patterns in case some helicopters are ruined.

**7**

*Sharing discoveries using* **ROUNDROBIN**

Allow time for students to return to their teams and **RoundRobin** their discoveries. Have them take turns sharing something they found out about their helicopter.

**8**

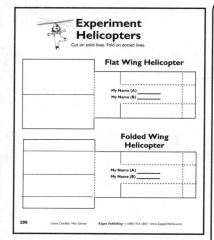

**Experiment Helicopters**

Cut on solid lines. Fold on dotted lines.

**Flat Wing Helicopter**

My Name (A) _____
My Name (B) _____

**Folded Wing Helicopter**

My Name (A) _____
My Name (B) _____

200    Laura Candler: *Wee Science*    *Kagan Publishing* • 1 (800) 933-2667 • www.KaganOnline.com

## *Making experiment helicopters using* PAIRS

**Materials for each Pair:**
 1 copy of Experiment Helicopters
 scissors
 tape
 pencil or pen

Within each pair of students, designate one partner as Person A and the other as Person B. Give each pair one copy of the Experiment Helicopters page. Tell them that they will be doing an experiment together and will use *both* helicopters. Stress the fact that *both* helicopters belong to both of the students. Remind students to say "our" helicopter not "my" helicopter.

Have them each cut out one helicopter. Tell them to write their names on both helicopters on the lines provided. If they have forgotten, remind them of who is Person A and Person B in each pair.

Have Person A make the Flat-Winged Helicopter just like the helicopters in the previous activity. Have Person B make the Folded-Wing Helicopter the same way and then fold up the edges of the wings on the dotted lines. The final helicopter will have two wing flaps (see illustration).

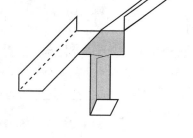

If your students have time, let them decorate their helicopters. Make sure the students take turns decorating both helicopters so they will feel ownership of *both* helicopters.

**SAFETY SPOTLIGHT**

Your students will want to test their helicopters by dropping them from a height. Standing on a chair is suitable and should pose no danger. However, you may want to let them test their helicopters by dropping them from a loft, balcony, stage, or other high location. If so, supervise the students carefully.

**9**

## Testing helicopters using RALLYTABLE

### Materials for each Pair:
1 Helicopter Experiment worksheet
2 crayons
1 folded and 1 flat-winged helicopter

### Step One: Making predictions
Now give each pair one copy of the Helicopter Experiment worksheet. Allow each person to choose one color crayon. Have each person write his or her name on the appropriate line and color the box with his or her chosen color.

Read the experiment question to them: *"Which helicopter will stay up longer?"* Ask them to decide if they think the folded or flat-wing helicopter will hit the ground last.

Tell them that they are going to do the experiment two times. Each time is called a **trial.** Have everyone put a finger on the word "prediction" for the first trial. Then have them use their own color to circle the helicopter which they think will stay up longer. Both can circle the same helicopter or they can each circle a different one.

### Step Two: Testing predictions
Now ask Person A to drop both helicopters at the same time from the same height. Person B should watch to see which helicopter stays up longer.

Observe your students carefully during this step. The flat-winged helicopter should always stay in the air longer. If not, have them repeat the experiment and make sure they are holding both helicopters the same way and are dropping them at the same time.

### Step Three: Recording results
Tell them both to circle the helicopter that stayed in the air longer.

### Step Four: Repeating the experiment
Repeat the same steps as above, but this time have Person B carry out the experiment while Person A watches.

---

**Helicopter Experiment**

Lesson 10

My Name (A) _____ My Color [ ]
My Name (B) _____ My Color [ ]

Which helicopter will stay up longer?

**First Trial**

| | Flat Wings | Folded Wings |
|---|---|---|
| **Predictions** | | |
| **Results** | | |

**Second Trial**

| | Flat Wings | Folded Wings |
|---|---|---|
| **Predictions** | | |
| **Results** | | |

*Kagan Publishing • 1 (800) 933-2667 • www.KaganOnline.com      Laura Candler: Wee Science      201*

---

## Discussing experiment results using **THINK-PAIR-SQUARE**

After everyone has finished, discuss the results with your students. Make sure they all understand that the flat-winged helicopter will always stay in the air longer than the one with folded wings.

Have each person think of their own explanation for why the flat-winged helicopter stayed up longer. Then have them pair and discuss their ideas with a partner. Next, ask them to "square" their ideas as a team. Finally, call on several students to share their teams' ideas with the class.

Several factors cause the flat-winged helicopter to stay in the air longer. First, its wings are wider which provides more surface area for the air to push up against. Second, it spins faster which helps to keep it in the air longer. The folds on the other helicopter's wings push against the flow of air which slows the spinning motion. As a result, the folded-wing helicopter drops quickly to the ground.

### Science Journal Ideas
**Vocabulary:** experiment, prediction, result, trial, helicopter, airplane
**Illustrations:** pictures of things that fly
**Writing:** explain why the the flat-wing helicopter stays up longer, explain the
difference between a helicopter and an airplane, explain the difference
between predictions and results

### For Younger Students
   Before the lesson, kindergarten teachers may want to cut out the helicopters and make the three inside cuts. Kindergarten students should be able to fold the helicopter on the lines while watching the teacher demonstrate, though some students will need help with this also.

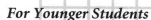

In classrooms with learning centers, the helicopters can be made by one team at a time during a visit to the Science Center. A teacher, assistant, or parent volunteer can help with the cutting and folding.

### For Older Students
Older students may enjoy participating in a Toy Helicopter Contest. Let them work in teams to design the helicopter that can stay up the longest. Students can change the basic design in any way. They can use any type of paper, change the size of the helicopter, add paperclips, glue on extra wings, or make any other modifications. Find a high place to test the final designs.

# Materials Check List

*For the Class:*
- ❏ 4 prepared posters of Things That Fly
- ❏ tape
- ❏ toy helicopter (optional)
- ❏ toy airplane (optional)
- ❏ 2 sheets of bond paper in different colors

*For each Student:*
- ❏ scrap paper
- ❏ pencil or crayon

*For each Team:*
- ❏ scissors
- ❏ crayons
- ❏ paper clips
- ❏ small bowl

*For each Pair:*
- ❏ 1 copy of Basic Helicopters
- ❏ 1 copy of Experiment Helicopters
- ❏ 1 Helicopter Experiment worksheet
- ❏ scissors
- ❏ pencil or pen
- ❏ tape
- ❏ 2 crayons

## Curriculum Links

**1. Social Studies - Studying about flight**
Teach your children about the invention of the airplane.

**2. Creative Movement - Pretending to be something that flies**
Clear a space in the room for children to move freely. Call out the name of one object that flies and have students move about the room pretending to be that object. Have them add sound effects also.

**3. Language Arts - Writing about flight**
Tell students to imagine that they can fly. What would they do and where would they go? Have them write and illustrate their stories.

**4. Math - Measuring airplane flight**
Teach your students how to fold a simple paper airplane. Then let team members experiment with their planes and discuss ways to make them fly farther. Let each team (or pair) try to design a plane that will fly farther than the original. Stage a contest to test the final designs. Have them measure the distance each airplane flew.

# Things That Fly

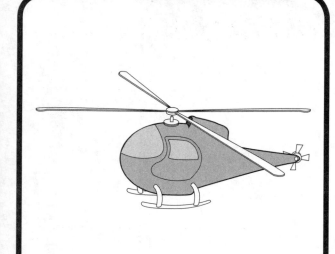

## Helicopter

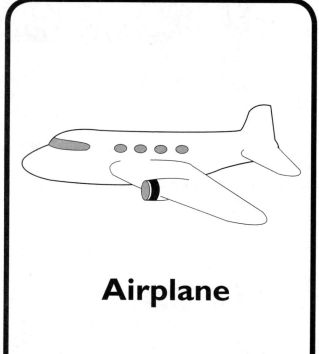

## Airplane

## Bird

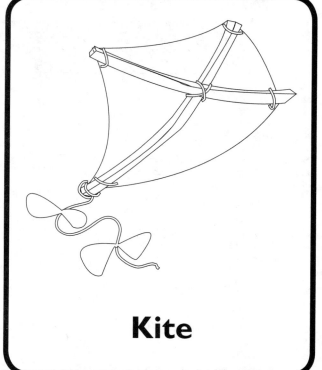

## Kite

Laura Candler: *Wee Science*    ***Kagan Publishing*** • 1 (800) 933-2667 • www.KaganOnline.com

# Basic Helicopters

Cut on solid lines. Fold on dotted lines.

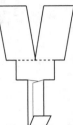

**My Name** _____

**My Name** _____

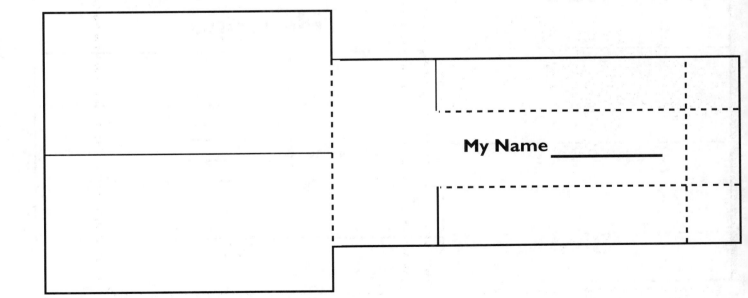

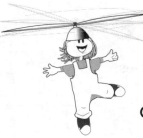

# Experiment Helicopters

Cut on solid lines. Fold on dotted lines.

## Flat Wing Helicopter

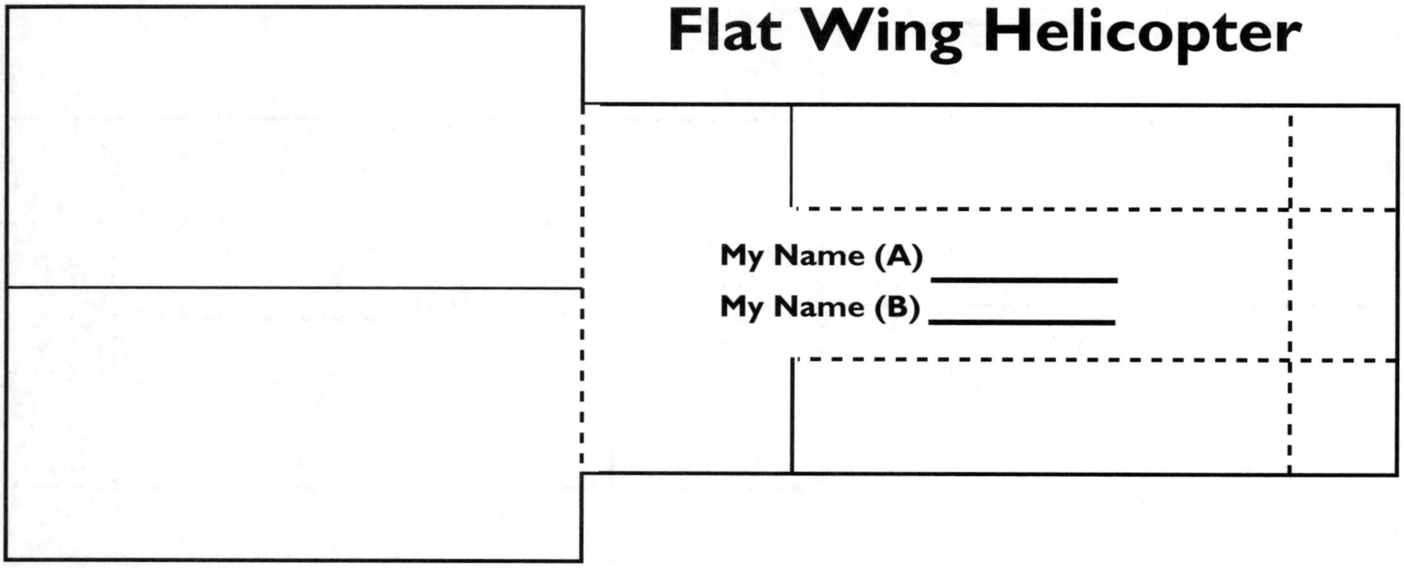

My Name (A) _____

My Name (B) _____

## Folded Wing Helicopter

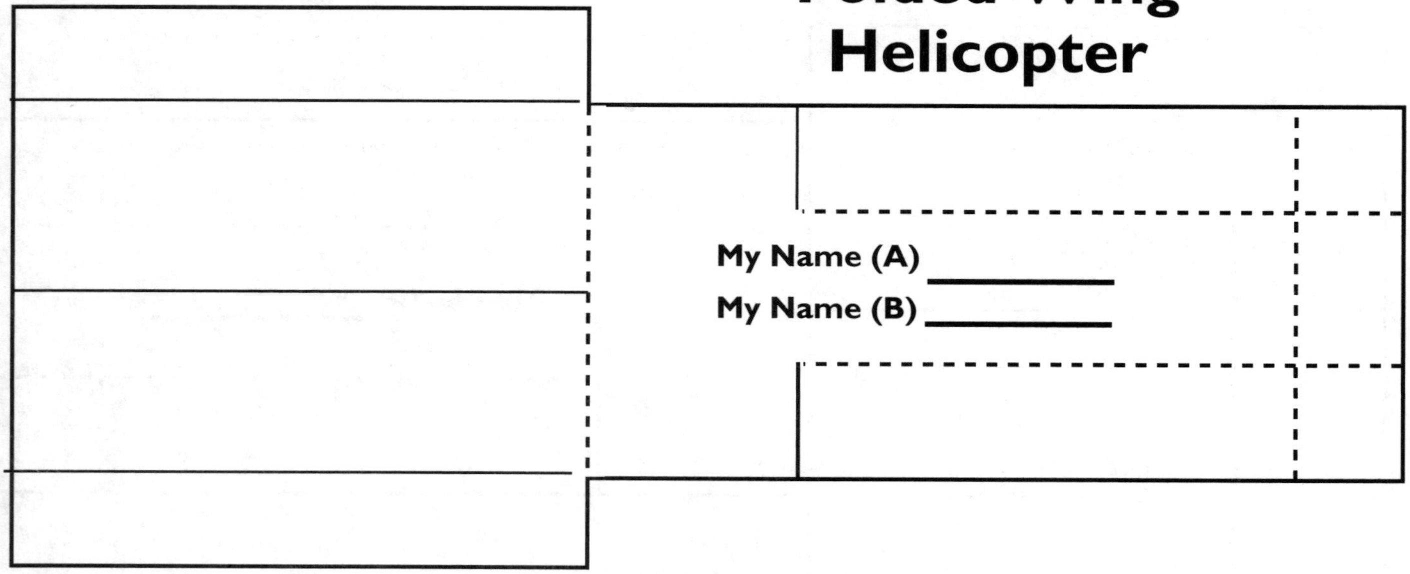

My Name (A) _____

My Name (B) _____

Laura Candler: *Wee Science*          ***Kagan Publishing*** • 1 (800) 933-2667 • www.KaganOnline.com

# Helicopter Experiment

My Name (A) _____ My Color [          ]

My Name (B) _____ My Color [          ]

## *Which helicopter will stay up longer?*

### First Trial

| | Flat Wings | Folded Wings |
|---|---|---|
| **Predictions** | | |
| **Results** | | |

### Second Trial

| | Flat Wings | Folded Wings |
|---|---|---|
| **Predictions** | | |
| **Results** | | |

Students Will...

Listen to *Everybody Needs a Rock*

Make team Rock Hunting Rule Books

Observe and describe rocks

Classify rocks

Line up according to rock characteristics

Weigh rocks

Process Skills...

Observing

Identifying

Classifying

Predicting

Measuring

Organizing Data

Communicating

Structures...

Cooperative Play

Line-Ups

Pairs

RoundRobin

RoundTable

Team Project

# Rounding Up
# Rocks

**R**ocks never cease to fascinate young children. They want to collect rocks, count them, sort them, and talk about them. This lesson gives your students the opportunity to satisfy their curiosity about rocks. The focus is on observing, classifying, and measuring rather than on identifying rocks by name. If you know the names of various types of rocks and minerals, share that information with your students informally. However, refrain from having them label rocks and memorize their names.

To begin the lesson, you'll read aloud *Everybody Needs a Rock,* a story in which a young rock collector describes ten rules for finding the perfect rock. Then your students will make up their own rules for finding rocks and will illustrate their ideas to create a team Rock Hunting Rule Book. They'll collect rocks and choose a special rock to observe carefully. With a partner, they'll classify their team rock collection. Later, team members will line up according to characteristics of their special rock. Finally, they'll weigh their rock and line up by its actual weight.

Some parts of this lesson can be completed by teams visiting a learning center. Note the circular learning center symbol next to these activities.

### Collect Rocks

Before starting this lesson, help each team collect at least a dozen rocks in an egg carton or small box. Have students bring in rocks from home and take them on a rock hunt around the school yard to find samples. Each team member should try to contribute at least 3 rocks to the team collection. Provide extra rocks to add variety to their collections. Your local lawn and garden store is a good source of rocks. You may be able to obtain free samples of marble, granite, volcanic lava, and limestone at such locations.

### Reading rock fiction using TEACHER READS

**Materials for the Class:**
*Everybody Needs a Rock* by Byrd Baylor

Read *Everybody Needs a Rock* aloud to your students. Before you read, say "Now that you have collected many rocks, what hints would you give someone who was going to hunt for a special rock?" Tell them to listen carefully to the author's ten rules for finding the perfect rock.

### 2

## *Making rock rule booklets using* TEAM PROJECT

**Materials for each Student:**
1 booklet page (lined or unlined)
1 pencil

**Materials for each Team:**
1 booklet cover (half sheet)
1 sheet of construction paper (9" × 12")
1 box of crayons
glue

**Materials for the Class:**
stapler

### *Step One: Sharing ideas*

Now ask your students to think about their own rock hunting rules. Ask "How would you tell someone to hunt for the perfect rock?" Let students suggest ideas and write their suggestions on the board.

When your students seem to understand the idea of "rock hunting rules," have them **RoundRobin** their own ideas within teams. Assign each team member a number from 1 to 4. Tell Person #1 to start by telling their team one rule for hunting rocks. Person #2 gives a rule next, followed by Person #3 and Person #4.

### *Step Two: Completing booklet pages*

Two types of booklet pages have been provided. One page has lines on which to write the rule, but the other is unlined for beginning writers. Choose the page that is most appropriate for your students.

Give each person one booklet page. Have each team member write their number in the box at the top of the page. Then tell them to write their rule on the lines below. Help with spelling or let them use inventive spelling. Finally, let them illustrate their rule by drawing a picture in the box at the bottom of the page.

(continued on page 206)

Our
R ck
Hunting
Rules

Rule # ☐

Rule # ☐

## 2 cont.

### *Making rock rule booklets* (continued from page 205)

#### Step Three: Making booklets

Give each team one booklet cover. Have each team member write his or her name on the inside of on rock. Then let them decorate the cover while you put their team booklet together.

To make the booklet, fold the construction paper in half and slip the four rule book pages inside. Staple the edge to hold the pages inside. Glue the decorated cover on the front of the rule book.

#### Step Four: Sharing rule books

Allow time for sharing the booklets with the class. Display them in a prominent location or leave them in a center for other students to enjoy. If time allows, do a **Team RoundRobin.** Everyone sits in a circle and each team comes forward to share their booklet with the class.

## 3

### *Playing with rocks using* **COOPERATIVE PLAY**

**Materials for each Team:**
  1 rock collection
  hand lenses

Give each team their rock collection and several hand lenses. Have them spread out all the rocks in front of them. Let them play with the rocks in an unstructured manner.

**4**

## Observing rocks using CLASS ROUNDROBIN

### Step One: Choosing a special rock

Now have each team member choose one rock from the team collection. Tell them to choose carefully because this will be their "special rock" to use in the next activity. If they all want the same rock, have them take turns choosing. Designate one person to choose first (for example, the shortest person or the one wearing the most green). Then let the person on their right choose the next rock and so on around the team. Give some consideration to students who brought special rocks from home. If children brought rocks to school, let them choose their own rocks.

### Step Two: Observing rocks

Have everyone bring their rock with them and sit in a class circle. Make sure you have a rock for yourself and join the circle. Ask your students to look carefully at their rocks to see how they are different from other rocks. Have them close their eyes and touch their rock all over with their fingers.

### Step Three: Sharing observations

Now have everyone open their eyes. Explain that they are going to take turns telling the class about their rock. Each person will say one sentence naming something they noticed about their rock. For example, someone might say, "My rock feels smooth all over," or "My rock has gray and white stripes." Explain that they are using their senses to make sentences which tell about the rock.

Start the **RoundRobin** by naming something about the rock you are holding. Then let the person on your left say something about their rock. Continue until everyone has shared an observation.

**5**

## Identifying rocks using CLASS ROUNDTABLE

### Step One: Passing rocks
While the class is still seated in a circle, ask your students if they think they could find their special rock if it was mixed in with many other rocks. Ask everyone to pass their rock to the person on their left. Have them continue passing rocks two or three more times.

### Step Two: Changing the order
Now have everyone get up and mix around the room without showing anyone the rock they are holding. On a signal, have them return to form a class circle again.

### Step Three: Identifying rocks
Now tell them to pass the rocks to their left again. Tell them that if they find their rock they should take it and sit outside of the circle. As the number of remaining students decreases, make the circle smaller. Continue passing rocks until everyone is sure they have their own.

**6**

## Classifying rocks using PAIRS

**Materials for each Team:**
  1 rock collection with 12 or more rocks

### Step One: Dividing the rock collection
Have everyone return to their team and place all the rocks back into the team collection. Then let them take turns choosing rocks to use for the next activity. Have them continue selecting rocks until all the rocks are divided among the team members. If there are a dozen rocks, each team member should end up with 3 rocks.

### Step Two: Classifying rocks
Assign partners who should sit next to each other with their rocks between them on the table or desk.

Ask your students to look at the rocks in front of them and figure out how they can group their small collection. Have them talk with their partner and decide one way the rocks can be grouped. After they agree, have them work together to move the rocks into those groups. If they don't understand what to do, model the activity with one pair of students. Show how the set of rocks can be grouped by color, size, or texture. Students can divide the rocks into two or more piles.

(continued on page 209)

## 6 cont.

### Classifying rocks (continued from page 208)

**Step Three: Discussing terms**
Introduce the words **sort** and **classify.** Explain that they have just "sorted" their rocks into different groups. Grouping things by the way those things are alike and different is called "classifying."

**Step Four: Guessing classification**
Now have each pair of students let their teammates try to guess how their rocks are classified.

**Step Five: Repeating the activity**
After teammates have correctly guessed each others' systems, have them work with their partner to classify their rocks in a different way. Continue classifying and guessing until students run out of ideas.

## 7

### Sequencing rocks using LINE-UPS

**Materials for each Team:**
- 1 rock collection with 12 or more rocks
- 1 sheet of plain paper
- 1 pencil or crayon

**Step One: Choosing a rock**
Have everyone choose another "special" rock. They may use the one they had before or select a different rock.

**Step Two: Lining up**
Now call out a characteristic and have each team do a "mini" line up of just four people. Team members hold their rock and line up according to their rock's unique characteristics. Ideas for Rock Line-Ups include:

> **Size: small ➔ large**
> **Texture: smooth ➔ rough**
> **Color: light ➔ dark**
> **Luster: shiny ➔ dull**

(continued on page 210)

## 7 cont.

### Sequencing rocks (continued from page 209)

#### Step Three: Lining up by rock weight

To prepare for the next activity, have students line up according to their rock's weight. Have team members line up from the lightest rock to the heaviest rock. They will probably have to hold each other's rocks to figure this out.

Give each team one piece of paper and have them draw a diagram of their positions. Have each person draw a circle and write their name in it to show their place in the line. Collect these and save them for the next activity.

**The Whiz Kids**

Tom　　Sue　　Maria　　Juan

## 8

### Weighing rocks using ROUNDTABLE

**Materials for each Team:**
I Rocky Weights worksheet
I rock collection
I balance
I set of weights (standard or non-standard)
I pencil

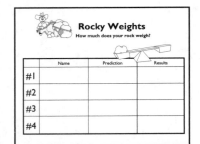

#### Step One: Explaining the activity

Depending on the skill level of your students, decide what kind of weights you want them to use in this activity. If possible, use a set of metric gram masses. If not, substitute non-standard weights such as pennies, marbles, or plastic bears.

Give each team a balance, set of weights, and a worksheet. Explain that they are going to take turns weighing their rocks. Before they weigh each rock, however, they will predict its weight. Tell them that a **prediction** is what they *think* will happen. Everyone will write their answers on the same worksheet.

(continued on page 211)

**8** cont.

### *Weighing rocks* (continued from page 210)

Show them how to use the balance and weights. To make sure everyone understands, let a few students come forward and weigh a rock (not their special rock).

### Step Two: Weighing rocks

Give each team a "Rocky Weights" worksheet. Have Person #1 on each team start by writing his or her name on the first line. Then ask them to tell their team how much they think their rock will weigh. After they say their prediction, have them write it in the space beside their name. Then have them weigh their rock and write down its weight. Have Persons #2, #3, and #4 continue predicting and weighing their rocks in turn.

### Step Three: Lining up by rock weight

Now have team members hold their rocks and line up according to actual rock weight. Show them the diagrams they drew of their first **Line-Up.** Did their **Line-Up** order change after they weighed their rocks?

### *Science Journal Suggestions*
**Vocabulary:** rock, sort, classify, prediction, balance, weight
**Illustrations:** pictures of favorite rocks, sketch of balance scale
**Writing:** rock hunting rules, descriptions of favorite rocks

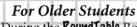

### *For Older Students*
During the **RoundTable** Rock Passing activity, older students may enjoy trying to identify their rock with their eyes closed. If this is too difficult with the entire class, divide the class into two or three smaller circles.

# Materials Check List

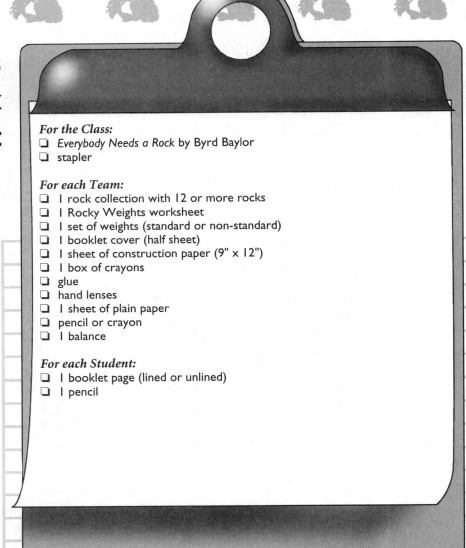

*For the Class:*
- ❏ *Everybody Needs a Rock* by Byrd Baylor
- ❏ stapler

*For each Team:*
- ❏ 1 rock collection with 12 or more rocks
- ❏ 1 Rocky Weights worksheet
- ❏ 1 set of weights (standard or non-standard)
- ❏ 1 booklet cover (half sheet)
- ❏ 1 sheet of construction paper (9" x 12")
- ❏ 1 box of crayons
- ❏ glue
- ❏ hand lenses
- ❏ 1 sheet of plain paper
- ❏ pencil or crayon
- ❏ 1 balance

*For each Student:*
- ❏ 1 booklet page (lined or unlined)
- ❏ 1 pencil

## Curriculum Links

### 1. Art - Decorating rocks
Let students paint their rocks and decorate them to make paper weights or "pet rocks."

### 2. Literature - Reading rock stories
Many fiction and nonfiction books have been written for children about rocks. Some fiction favorites are *The Big Rock* by Bruce Hiscock and *How to Dig a Hole to the Other Side of the Earth* by Faith McNulty. *Magic School Bus Inside the Earth* by Joanna Cole is a wacky but informative story that is also available on videotape as a part of the Reading Rainbow series. *Rock Collecting* by Roma Gans is an excellent nonfiction book for students who are interested in learning more.

### 3. Science - Guessing rocks
Older students can play "Guess My Rock." Each team member places four rocks on his or her desk and mentally picks one as his or her "special" rock. In **Team Interview** style, each person takes a turn having the other team members ask questions to figure out which one is the special rock.

### 4. Math - Sorting with Venn diagrams
Teach students how to sort their rocks using Venn diagrams. Place two hula-hoops on the floor so that they overlap. Have everyone select a rock to bring with them as they form a large circle around the two hoops. Use paper labels to identify two attributes and let each student come forward and place his or her rock in the correct spot. Some attribute combinations to try are:

*Rough and Shiny*
*White and Smooth*
*Speckled and Large*

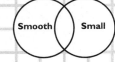

Laura Candler: *Wee Science*      **Kagan Publishing** • 1 (800) 933-2667 • www.KaganOnline.com

# Rocky Weights

## How much does your rock weigh?

| | Name | Prediction | Results |
|---|---|---|---|
| **#1** | | | |
| **#2** | | | |
| **#3** | | | |
| **#4** | | | |

**Our Rock Hunting Rules**

**Our Rock Hunting Rules**

**Rule #**

**Rule #**

Rule #

Rule #

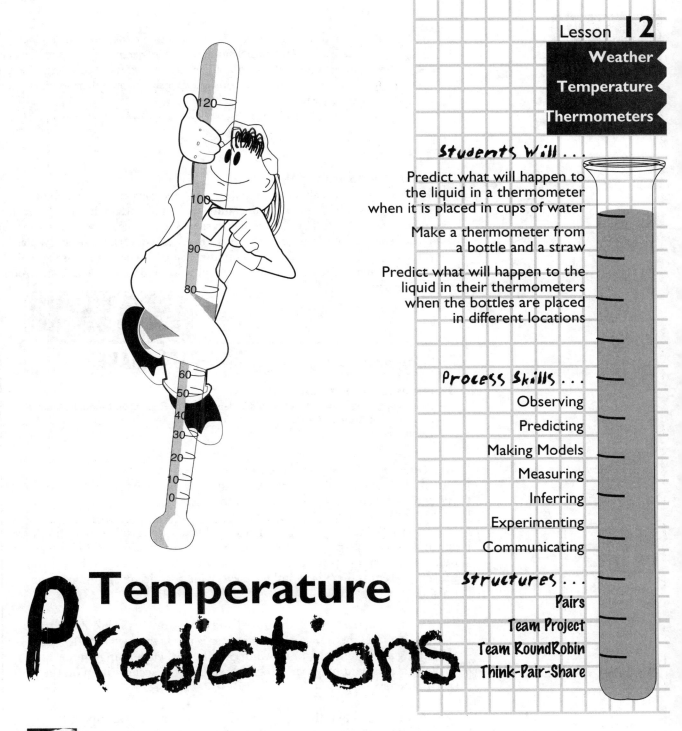

### Students Will . . .

Predict what will happen to the liquid in a thermometer when it is placed in cups of water

Make a thermometer from a bottle and a straw

Predict what will happen to the liquid in their thermometers when the bottles are placed in different locations

### Process Skills . . .

Observing

Predicting

Making Models

Measuring

Inferring

Experimenting

Communicating

### Structures . . .

Pairs

Team Project

Team RoundRobin

Think-Pair-Share

# Temperature Predictions

**T**he objective of this lesson is not to teach students how to read a thermometer. Instead, the focus is on predicting what will happen to the liquid in a thermometer when it is placed in various locations. After using commercial thermometers, students will make simple thermometers from soda bottles, water, clay, and straws. They will learn that thermometers are not magic, since these homemade instruments work the same way as commercial thermometers.

SAFETY SPOTLIGHT

Most commercial thermometers now contain alcohol rather than mercury. Avoid using mercury thermometers since mercury is a poison that can be absorbed through the skin. If you are unsure about the thermometers you are using, purchase some inexpensive alcohol thermometers from a science supply catalog.

### Prepare Containers of Water

Prepare four separate half-gallon containers of water, each having a different temperature of water. The exact temperatures are not important; however, no container should have water that is hot enough to hurt small fingers. Suggested temperatures are: room temperature, cold, ice cold, and very warm water. For each team, label 4 plastic cups with the letters A, B, C, and D. A few minutes before you begin the lesson, fill the cups with water. Pour cold water in cup A, very warm water in B, ice cold water in cup C, and room temperature water in cup D.

**1**

## Making predictions using THINK-PAIR-SHARE

### Materials for each Team:
4 plastic cups of water (each cup should be labeled A, B, C, or D and should contain a different temperature of water)
1 thermometer

### Step One: Introducing the thermometer
Distribute the materials to each team. All team members should be close enough to the cups of water to be able to touch them.

Hold up a thermometer and ask if anyone knows what is. Let them think about their own responses, then pair with a partner to discuss their ideas. Call on a few students to share their ideas with the class. Write the word **thermometer** on the board and have everyone practice pronouncing it in unison.

Then write **temperature** on the board and have students **Think-Pair-Share** its meaning. Tell them that a thermometer is used when we need to know something's temperature, or how hot or cold it is. Depending on the age of the students, you may want to briefly discuss the scale written on the thermometer.

Tell your students that the liquid in the thermometer moves up and down when the temperature changes. Ask Person #1 to gently place his or her finger on the bulb of the thermometer. Ask everyone on the team to observe carefully. Have them **Think-Pair-Share** their observations.

### Step Two: Making a prediction
Write the word **predict** on the board. Tell your students that "predict" means to say what you think will happen before you do something. Tell them that they are going to predict what will happen to the liquid in the thermometer when they place it in each cup.

(continued on page 219)

## **1 cont.**

### *Making predictions* (continued from page 218)

Now ask everyone to place a finger into cup A for about 10 seconds. Ask them to predict what will happen to the liquid in the thermometer when it is placed into the cup. Have them think about their own responses. Then teach them three hand signals to use when making their predictions:

1. **Thumbs up if they think the liquid will go up**
2. **Thumbs down if they think the liquid will go down**
3. **Thumbs sideways if they think the liquid will stay the same.**

Count to three, and then have everyone simultaneously turn to their partner and make a prediction by showing their hand signals. Call on a few students to share responses with the class.

### *Step Three: Testing predictions*
Now have Person #1 place the thermometer in the cup. Ask everyone to watch the liquid until it stops moving (about 30 seconds). Discuss the results.

### *Step Four: Continue making and testing predictions*
Have everyone place a finger in cup B, then **Think-Pair-Share** their predictions (using hand-signals). Then have Person #2 place the thermometer in the cup so that everyone can observe the results. Continue with cups C and D. Allow a different student to handle the thermometer during each round of testing.

### *Step Five: Discussing results*
Ask students to **Think-Pair-Share** what happened to the liquid in the thermometer when it was placed in cold water. Then have them do the same for hot water placement. Make sure all students understand that the level of liquid rises in hot water and falls in cold water. You may want to explain to older students that the reason is the molecules in a liquid speed up and move farther apart when heated. This action causes the level of the liquid to rise. When cooled, the same molecules slow down and move closer together. The result is that the level of the liquid falls. Students tend to think that a thermometer works by "magic." The next activity will show them that even water in a homemade thermometer behaves like alcohol in a commercial thermometer.

Since the bottles used in Activity 2 are made of glass, extra precautions must be taken. Students should construct the water thermometers on a flat surface to keep the bottles from accidentally rolling off. You may even want to have students sit on the floor while making the thermometers to minimize the danger of bottles dropping. Ask students to hold their thermometers firmly with both hands when they are carrying them to a new location. Tell them that if a bottle breaks to let you know and **NOT** to try to clean up the glass themselves.

## Collect Materials

Make sure you have one soda bottle (16–20 ounce size) for each pair of students. The bottles must be glass, not plastic, so you should not ask students to bring them from home. You will also need a bottle for yourself so that you can demonstrate the procedure. Several hours before the lesson, fill each bottle with water to a level about 2 inches from the top. *Allow the water to reach room temperature before beginning the lesson.* Clear plastic straws are needed for making these thermometers. If you can't find them in the grocery store, try checking local restaurants. If you are unable to find clear straws, use white ones and color the water very dark.

## 2

### Making a soda-bottle thermometer using PAIRS

**Materials for each Pair:**
I glass soda bottle (16 - 20 ounce size) filled
   with room temperature water
I clear plastic straw
I lump modeling clay (about a cubic inch)

**Materials for each Team:**
red, green or blue food coloring
eyedropper
cup of water
overhead projector pen

### Step One: Explaining the activity

Tell your students that they will work with a partner to make a simple thermometer. Divide your teams of four into two sets of partners and give them all their materials. Ask them to watch you as you make yours, and to work together to make theirs at the same time.

Very young children will need help constructing their thermometers. If your classroom is set up with learning centers, you may want to have each team rotate to your Science Center to make their thermometers. Or have your students come one team at a time to a workstation while other students are completing assignments at their desks. If you are unable to stay at the workstation during this activity, recruit a parent volunteer or teacher assistant to help.

(continued on page 221)

## 2 cont.

***Making a soda-bottle thermometer*** (continued from page 220)
**Step Two: Making the thermometer**

1. Drop 5 drops of one color food coloring in the top of the bottle. (Younger students will need you to do this for them.) You do not need to stir the water since the food coloring will spread on its own.

2. Roll the modeling clay into a fat "snake" about 2 inches long. Connect the ends to form a doughnut. Place the doughnut on the rim of the bottle.

3. Place the straw into the bottle so that the bottom of the straw is about an inch below the surface of the water. Most of the straw should be above the opening of the bottle.

4. Pinch the clay around the straw to seal the opening. *You must have an airtight seal or the thermometer will not work.* You can tell that the clay has sealed the opening if a small amount of water rises into the straw. This is the most difficult step, and many students will need help to ensure a tight seal. Sometimes the clay will become so wet and slippery that students will need to start over with a new lump of clay.

5. Drop several drops of the same color food coloring into the cup of water and stir with the eyedropper.

6. Now use the eyedropper to add water to the top of the straw until the water level is about an inch above the top of the bottle.

7. Use the overhead projector pen to mark the water level on the straw. Be sure the pen is nonpermanent so the ink can be easily rubbed off.

clay

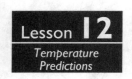

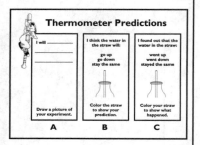

**3**

## Experimenting with soda bottle thermometers *using* TEAM PROJECT

**Materials for each Team:**
2 soda bottle thermometers
Thermometer Predictions worksheets (at least 1 per person)
crayons
pie pan or tray

### Step One: Explaining the project
Tell your students that they will work as a team to experiment with their thermometers. Give each person on the team one Thermometer Predictions worksheet.

### Step Two: Team Discussion
Ask students to think of things they could do to their thermometers to try to make the level of the water change. Write their ideas on the board. Then let each team have a brief **Team Discussion** in which they choose the one idea they want to use in their experiment. Some ideas are:

- placing their hands on the bottle
- placing the bottle in a bucket of ice water
- placing the bottle in a refrigerator
- placing the bottle outside in the sun
- placing the bottle outside in the shade
- placing the bottle on top of a cabinet
- placing the bottle on top of a vent

### Step Three: Placing the bottles
Each team should have **two** soda bottle thermometers. Make sure each straw has a pen mark to show the current water level.

Have Persons #1 and #2 carefully place the bottles in the location agreed upon by the team. Bottles placed in warm locations should be placed on a pan or tray, because they will often overflow when heated excessively.

(continued on page 223)

## 3 cont.

### Experimenting with soda bottle thermometers
(continued from page 222)

**Step Four: Completing the first two sections of the worksheet**
Now have everyone find Section A of their worksheet and draw a picture of their experiment. They should also write a description of the experiment on the lines provided, using the words on the board as a guide.

Remind your students that a prediction is what they think is going to happen. Ask them "What is your prediction about what will happen to the water in the straw? Do you think the water will go up, go down, or stay the same height?" They may discuss their ideas with their team, but everyone should make their own prediction. Ask everyone to find the Section B of their worksheet. Have them circle the phrase that describes their prediction. Then have them color in the predicted height of the water in the straw.

**Step Five: Discovering and recording results**
By the time students complete the first two sections of the worksheet, the thermometers should have been in place long enough show a new temperature.

Ask Persons #3 and #4 to carefully bring the bottles back to the team. Show them how to compare the new temperature with the mark on the straw.

Now ask everyone to find Section C on their worksheets. Have them circle the phrase that describes their results. Then ask them to draw a picture of what really happened to the water level in the straw.

**4**

### Sharing results using TEAM ROUNDROBIN

Now ask the entire class to gather in a large circle. Have each team sit together with their soda bottle thermometers and worksheets in front of them.

Tell your students that one person from each team will be a Reporter who will tell the class about their team's experiment. Tell them that they won't know who the Reporter will be until it's time to give the team report, so they need to make sure everyone can answer the following questions. Write the questions on the board and read them to the class:

**Where did your team put their bottles?**
**What did you predict would happen?**
**What really happened?**

When all the teams are ready, call on one person from each team to tell the class about their experiment, using the questions as a guide.

### Science Journal Suggestions
**Vocabulary:** thermometer, temperature, predict
**Illustrations:** drawing their thermometers, sketching the location of their experiment
**Writing:** explain the experiment, tell whether their predictions were correct, explain what happens to the liquid in a thermometer when the temperature gets hotter or colder

### For Older Students
Use this lesson as an opportunity to introduce the Celsius or Fahrenheit thermometer. On the board or overhead projector, draw a picture of the type of thermometer your class will be using. Explain how to interpret the thermometer's scale. During the part of the lesson involving the four cups of water, have students predict the actual temperatures then use their thermometers to measure the water temperatures exactly.

# Materials Check List

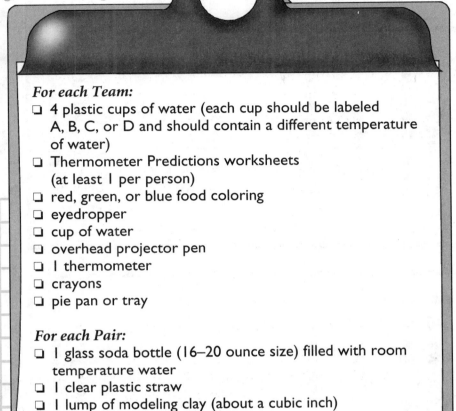

### For each Team:

❑ 4 plastic cups of water (each cup should be labeled A, B, C, or D and should contain a different temperature of water)

❑ Thermometer Predictions worksheets (at least 1 per person)

❑ red, green, or blue food coloring

❑ eyedropper

❑ cup of water

❑ overhead projector pen

❑ 1 thermometer

❑ crayons

❑ pie pan or tray

### For each Pair:

❑ 1 glass soda bottle (16–20 ounce size) filled with room temperature water

❑ 1 clear plastic straw

❑ 1 lump of modeling clay (about a cubic inch)

## Curriculum Links

### 1. Math - Graphing daily temperature

Place a thermometer in a shady outdoor location. Send teams of students to read the temperature at the same time each day. Show students how to plot the temperatures on a line graph.

### 2. Science - Experiencing a temperature mystery

Prepare three bowls of water: very warm, room temperature, and ice cold. Have one child at a time place one hand in the warm water and one hand in the cold water. Leave hands in place for one minute. When the time is up, have the student quickly plunge both hands into the bowl of room temperature water. Ask them if the water is hot or cold. Strangely enough, they will receive mixed signals. The hand that was in cold water will feel that the water is warm, and the other hand will experience it as cold!

### 3. Health - Learning about different thermometers

Bring several different types of thermometers for children to observe. Digital thermometers are often used to take a person's temperature when sick. Liquid crystal thermometers are often used to measure air or water temperature (some bath toys have this type of thermometer built in to check water temperature.)

# Thermometer Predictions

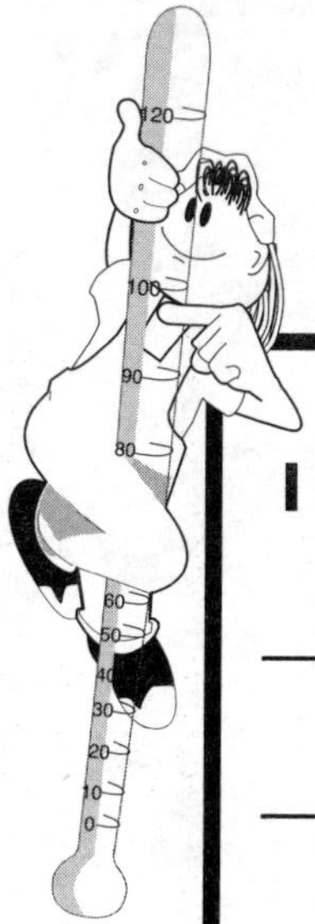

## A

I will _____

_____

_____

**Draw a picture of your experiment.**

## B

I think the water in the straw will:

go up
go down
stay the same

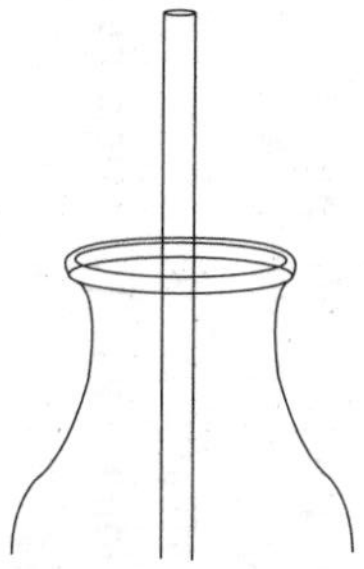

**Color the straw to show your prediction.**

## C

I found out that the water in the straw:

went up
went down
stayed the same

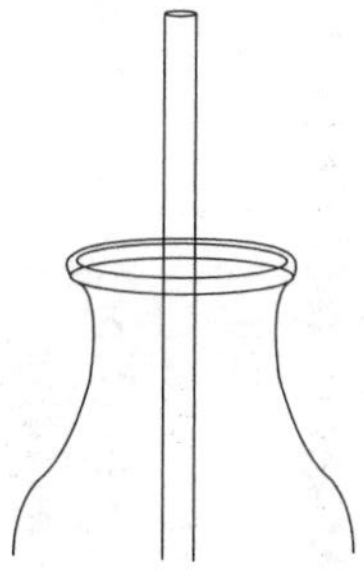

**Color your straw to show what happened.**

## Professional Organizations

### National Science Teachers Association (NSTA)

National Science Teachers
Association
1840 Wilson Blvd.
Arlington, VA 22201
(703) 243-7100

NSTA provides many resources to science teachers at all grade levels. Membership in the organization entitles you to a subscription of *Science and Children, Science Scope, The Science Teacher,* or the *Journal of College Science Teaching.* NSTA also publishes a wealth of materials designed to help the science teacher. The organization sponsors regional and national conventions which provide teachers with up-to-date information and new teaching ideas.

### American Association for the Advancement of Science (AAAS)

American Association for the
Advancement of Science
1333 H Street, N.W.
Washington, DC 20005
(202) 326-6400

The AAAS is sponsoring Project 2061, a plan for science education reform. The first two phases are currently complete and are described in two publications: *Science for All Americans* and *Benchmarks for Science Literacy.* Write to Project 2061 at the above address.

## Science Material Suppliers

The following companies supply books and/or materials to science educators. Write on school letterhead or call to obtain a catalog.

**Carolina Biological Supply Co.**
2700 York Road
Burlington, NC 26215
(800) 334-5551

**Delta Education, Inc.**
P.O. Box 915
Hudson, NH 03051
(800) 258-1302

**Idea Factory, Inc.**
10710 Dixon Drive
Riverview, FL 33569
(800) 331-6204

**NASCO**
P. O. Box 901
Fort Atkinson, WI 53538
(800) 558-9595

**Sargent-Welch Scientific Co.**
911 Commerce Court
Buffalo Grove, IL 60089
(800) SARGENT

**Schoolmasters Science**
745 State Circle
Box 1941
Ann Arbor, MI 48106
(800) 521-2832

# Bibliography of Children's Literature

**Adams, Georgie.** *Fish Fish Fish.* New York, NY: Dial Books for Young Readers, 1993.

**Baylor, Byrd.** *Everybody Needs a Rock.* New York, NY: Scribner, 1974.

**Campbell, Rod.** *My Presents.* New York, NY: Macmillan, 1989.

**Carle, Eric.** *A Tiny Seed.* Natick, MA: Picture Book Studio, 1987.

**Cherry, Lynne.** *The Great Kapok Tree.* San Diego, CA: Harcourt Brace Jovanovich, 1990.

**Cole, Joanna.** *Magic School Bus Inside the Earth.* New York, NY: Scholastic, Inc., 1987.

**Dorros, Arthur.** *Rain Forest Secrets.* New York, NY: Scholastic, Inc., 1990.

**Ehlert, Lois.** *Red Leaf, Yellow Leaf.* San Diego, CA: Harcourt Brace Jovanovich, 1991.

**Freeman, Don.** *A Rainbow of My Own.* New York, NY: Viking Press, 1966.

**Gans, Roma.** *Rock Collecting.* New York, NY: Harper & Row, 1986.

**Gibbons, Gail.** *From Seed to Plant.* New York, NY: Holiday House, 1991.

**Heller, Ruth.** *The Reason For a Flower.* New York, NY: Grosset & Dunlap, 1983.

**Hiscock, Bruce.** *The Big Rock.* New York, NY: Atheneum, 1988.

**McNulty, Faith.** *How to Dig a Hole to the Other Side of the Earth.* New York, NY: Harper & Row, 1979.

**O'Neill, Mary.** *Hailstones and Halibut Bones: Adventures in Color.* New York, NY: Doubleday, 1989.

**Pfister, Marcus.** *The Rainbow Fish.* New York, NY: North-South Books Inc., 1992.

**Selsam, Millicent and Joyce Hunt.** *A First Look at Leaves.* New York, NY: Walker, 1972.

**Showers, Paul.** *The Listening Walk.* New York, NY: HarperCollins, 1991.

**Udry, Janice.** *A Tree is Nice.* New York, NY: HarperCollins, 1987.

**Yolen, Jane.** *Welcome to the Greenhouse.* New York, NY: G. P. Putnam, 1993.

# Notes

Laura Candler: *Wee Science*          ***Kagan Publishing*** • 1 (800) 933-2667 • www.KaganOnline.com

# Notes

# Notes

# Notes

# Notes